The Secret Garden
秘密花园

■ Frances Hodgson Burnett 〔英〕 著

■ Clare West 〔英〕 改写

■ 郑志红 译

外语教学与研究出版社
FOREIGN LANGUAGE TEACHING AND RESEARCH PRESS
北京 BEIJING

京权图字 01－97－0338

Originally published by Oxford University Press, Great Clarendon Street, Oxford.
© 1993
This edition is licensed for sale in the People's Republic of China only and not for export therefrom.
'Oxford' is a registered trademark of Oxford University Press.

图书在版编目(CIP)数据

秘密花园 = The Secret Garden / (英)伯内特(Burnett, F.H.)著; (英)韦斯特(West, C.)改写; 郑志红译 .— 北京: 外语教学与研究出版社, 1997.10
(2007.3 重印)
(书虫·牛津英汉双语读物)
ISBN 978－7－5600－1301－5

Ⅰ. 秘… Ⅱ. ①伯… ②韦… ③郑… Ⅲ. 小说—对照读物—英、汉
Ⅳ. H319.4：I

中国版本图书馆 CIP 数据核字 (97) 第 18052 号

出 版 人：李朋义
责任编辑：周　晶
出版发行：外语教学与研究出版社
社　　址：北京市西三环北路 19 号 (100089)
网　　址：http://www.fltrp.com
印　　刷：北京一二零一印刷厂
开　　本：850×1092　1/32
印　　张：3.25
版　　次：1998 年 1 月第 1 版　2007 年 3 月第 11 次印刷
书　　号：ISBN 978－7－5600－1301－5
定　　价：3.90 元
＊　　　＊　　　＊
如有印刷、装订质量问题出版社负责调换
制售盗版必究 举报查实奖励
版权保护办公室举报电话：(010)88817519

简　介

　　"咱俩差不多，"本·威瑟斯塔夫老头对玛丽说，"长得丑，脾气也不好。"

　　可怜的玛丽！谁都不要她，也没人喜欢她。父母去世以后，她被人从印度送回英国的约克郡，住在她舅舅的家里。那是一幢旧房子，很大，差不多有上百个房间，可大部分都关得严严实实，还上了锁。玛丽住在那儿，情绪很坏，她感到厌烦、孤独，整天没事可做，除了园丁本·威瑟斯塔夫老头，没人跟她说说话。

　　不过后来玛丽听说了有关秘密花园的事。那花园的门紧锁着，钥匙也不知哪儿去了。10 年了，除了那只能够飞过围墙的知更鸟，没有一个人进过那园子。玛丽望着知更鸟，琢磨着钥匙会在哪儿……

　　再后来，夜里房子中什么地方传来奇怪的哭声，听起来像是个孩子……

　　弗朗西丝·霍奇森·伯内特生于 1849 年，卒于 1924 年。从 16 岁起她大部分时间住在美国，但经常回英格兰。她是一位终身作家，写了很多书，《秘密花园》是她的代表作。

1

Little Miss Mary

Nobody seemed to care about Mary. She was born in India, where her father was a British official. He was busy with his work, and her mother, who was very beautiful, spent all her time going to parties. So an Indian woman, Kamala, was paid to take care of the little girl. Mary was not a pretty child. She had a thin angry face and thin yellow hair. She was always giving orders to Kamala, who had to obey. Mary never thought of other people, but only of herself. In fact, she was a very selfish, disagreeable, bad-tempered little girl.

One very hot morning, when she was about nine years old, she woke up and saw that instead of Kamala there was a different Indian servant by her bed.

'What are *you* doing here?' she asked crossly. 'Go away! And send Kamala to me at once!'

The woman looked afraid. 'I'm sorry, Miss Mary, she — she — she can't come!'

Something strange was happening that day. Some of the house servants were missing and everybody looked frightened. But nobody told Mary anything, and Kamala still did not come. So at last Mary went out into the garden, and played by herself under a tree. She pretended she was making her own flower garden, and picked large red flowers to push into the

2

1 幼年的玛丽小姐

　　似乎没有人注意玛丽的存在。玛丽出生在印度,父亲是驻印的英国官员,总是忙着工作,母亲长得非常漂亮,把所有时间都花在参加聚会上。所以,一个名叫卡玛拉的印度女人被雇来照看这个小姑娘。玛丽长得不漂亮,消瘦的脸上总是一副生气的样子,头发稀疏枯黄。她总对卡玛拉发号施令,卡玛拉只好顺从她。她很少想到别人,只顾自己。她确实是一个非常自私,脾气怪戾,很难相处的小女孩。

　　在她大约9岁那年的一个上午,天气很热,她醒来时发现站在床前的不是卡玛拉,而是另外一个印度女仆。

　　"你在这儿干什么?"她生气地问,"走开!叫卡玛拉马上到这儿来!"

　　那个女人看来很害怕。"对不起,玛丽小姐,她——她——她来不了了!"

　　那天发生了一些很奇怪的事情,房子里的一些仆人不见了,每个人看上去都惊恐异常。可是没有人告诉玛丽任何事情,卡玛拉也始终没来。最后玛丽只好一个人来到花园,在一棵树下玩耍。她假装是在给自己造一座花园,摘来大朵的红花插在土里,一边

official *n. a person holding office or engaged in official duties.* 官员。**disagreeable** *adj. unpleasant; rude.* 让人讨厌的,不友善的。**crossly** *adv. having a bad temper.* 不高兴地,执拗地。**pretend** *v. behave in a particular way because you want someone to believe that something is true when it is not.* 假装,装作。

ground. All the time she was saying crossly to herself,

'I hate Kamala! I'll hit her when she comes back!'

Just then she saw her mother coming into the garden, with a young Englishman. They did not notice the child, who listened to their conversation.

'It's very bad, is it?' her mother asked the young man in a worried voice.

'Very bad,' he answered seriously. 'People are dying like flies. It's dangerous to stay in this town. You should go to the hills, where there's no disease.'

'Oh, I know!' she cried. 'We must leave soon!'

Suddenly they heard loud cries coming from the servants' rooms, at the side of the house.

'What's happened?' cried Mary's mother wildly.

'I think one of your servants has just died. You didn't tell me the disease is *here*, in your house!'

'I didn't know!' she screamed. 'Quick, come with me!' And together they ran into the house.

Now Mary understood what was wrong. The terrible disease had already killed many people in the town, and in all the houses people were dying. In Mary's house it was Kamala who had just died. Later that day three more servants died there.

All through the night and the next day people ran in and out of the house, shouting and crying. Nobody thought of Mary. She hid in her bedroom, frightened by the strange and terrible sounds that she heard around her. Sometimes she cried and

玩还一边堵气地自言自语:

"我讨厌卡玛拉!等她回来我要揍她一顿!"

就在这会儿,她看见妈妈和一个年轻的英国人走进花园,玛丽听见了他们的谈话,他们却没注意到她。

"很严重,是吗?"妈妈问那个年轻人,声音充满焦虑。

"非常严重,"他严肃地说,"人们像苍蝇一样死去,再在城里待下去太危险了,你得到山里去,那里没有疫病。"

"哦,我知道!"她叫道,"我们得马上离开!"

突然,他们听到房子侧面用人屋里传来嚎啕大哭的声音。

"出了什么事?"玛丽的妈妈慌乱地大叫着。

"我看是你的一个用人刚刚死去。你没告诉过我这儿也有疫病,在你的房子里!"

"我根本不知道!"她尖声叫着,"快,跟我来。"他们一同冲进屋去。

现在玛丽明白是哪儿不对了。可怕的疫病已经夺去了城里很多人的生命,到处都有人在死去。在玛丽家刚刚死去的正是卡玛拉。那天后来又有3个用人死了。

整整一夜到第二天,人们跑进跑出,哭着,喊着,谁也没想起玛丽。她躲在卧室里,被周围这些可怕的奇怪声音吓坏了,不时

sometimes she slept.

When she woke the next day, the house was silent.

'Perhaps the disease has gone,' she thought, 'and everybody is well again. I wonder who will take care of me instead of Kamala? Why doesn't someone bring me some food? It's strange the house is so quiet.'

But just then she heard men's voices in the hall.

'How sad!' said one. 'That beautiful woman!'

'There was a child too, wasn't there?' said the other. 'Although none of us ever saw her.'

Mary was standing in the middle of her room when they opened the door a few minutes later. The two men jumped back in surprise.

'My name is Mary Lennox,' she said crossly. 'I was asleep when everyone was ill, and now I'm hungry.'

'It's the child, the one nobody ever saw!' said the older man to the other. 'They've all forgotten her!'

'*Why* was I forgotten?' asked Mary angrily. '*Why* has nobody come to take care of me?'

The younger man looked at her very sadly. 'Poor child!' he said. 'You see, there's nobody left alive in the house. So nobody *can* come.'

In this strange and sudden way Mary learnt that both her mother and her father had died. The few servants who had not died had run away in the night. No one had remembered little Miss Mary. She was all alone.

地哭着,哭累了就睡上一会儿。

第二天,当她醒来时,房子里一片寂静。

"说不定疫病已经过去,"她想着,"人们又和从前一样健康了,谁会接替卡玛拉来照看我呢?为什么家里没人给我送点吃的来?房子里这么静,真是太奇怪了。"

就在这时,她听到客厅里男人说话的声音。

"太惨啦!"有人说,"这么漂亮的女人!"

"还应该有个孩子的,是不是?"另外一个人说,"尽管我们都没有看见她。"

几分钟后,他们推开门,玛丽站在房间的中央,两个男人吓得跳了回去。

"我叫玛丽·莲诺丝,"她生气地说,"他们生病时我睡着了,现在我很饿。"

"就是这个孩子,谁都没看见她!"年长一点的男人对另一个说,"他们都把她忘了!"

"为什么把我忘了?"玛丽气呼呼地问,"为什么没人来照看我?"

年轻一点的男人忧伤地看着她,"可怜的孩子!"他说,"听着,这幢房子里的人全死了,所以没有人能来照看你。"

以这样一种奇异而突然的方式,玛丽得知她的父母已不在人世,活下来的几个用人也趁半夜逃走了。没人想起年幼的玛丽小姐,就只剩下她一个人了。

untidy adj. not neat and tidy. 不整洁的。**crooked** adj. not straight. 驼的,弯的。

Because she had never known her parents well, she did not miss them at all. She only thought of herself, as she had always done.

'Where will I live?' she wondered. 'I hope I'll stay with people who'll let me do what I want.'

At first she was taken to an English family who had known her parents. She hated their untidy house and noisy children, and preferred playing by herself in the garden. One day she was playing her favourite game, pretending to make a garden, when one of the children, Basil, offered to help.

'Go away!' cried Mary. 'I don't want your help!'

For a moment Basil looked angry, and then he began to laugh. He danced round and round Mary, and sang a funny little song about Miss Mary and her stupid flowers. This made Mary very cross indeed. No one had ever laughed at her so unkindly.

'You're going home soon,' said Basil. 'And we're all very pleased you're leaving!'

'I'm pleased too,' replied Mary. 'But where's home?'

'You're stupid if you don't know that!' laughed Basil. 'England, of course! You're going to live with your uncle, Mr Archibald Craven.'

'I've never heard of him,' said Mary coldly.

'But *I* know about him because I heard Father and Mother talking,' said Basil. 'He lives in a big lonely old house, and has no friends, because he's so bad-tempered. He's got a crooked

8

由于她跟父母并不亲近,因此一点也不想念他们。像以前一样,她只想到了她自己。

　　"我该住哪儿呢?"她思量着,"我想跟那些让我想干什么就干什么的人在一起。"

　　一开始她被带到一户英国人家,他们认识她的父母。可她讨厌他们凌乱的房子和吵吵闹闹的孩子们,而宁愿一个人在花园里玩。一天,她正玩着最喜欢的造花园游戏,那家的孩子巴兹尔走过来想帮她忙。

　　"走开!"玛丽大声喊道,"我才不用你帮忙!"

　　巴兹尔呆站了一会儿,很生气,可很快又乐开了。他围着玛丽又蹦又跳,一边唱起一支滑稽的有关玛丽小姐和她愚蠢的花儿的歌。这可把玛丽气坏了,还从来没人这么刻薄地嘲笑过她呢!

　　"你就快回家了,"巴兹尔说,"我们真高兴你快走了。"

　　"我也高兴,"玛丽答道,"可回哪儿的家?"

　　"你连这都不知道,可真够傻的!"巴兹尔笑道,"当然是英国! 你要去跟你舅舅阿奇伯德·克莱文先生住了!"

　　"我从来没听说过他。"玛丽冷冷地说。

　　"可我知道,我听我爸爸妈妈谈论过他。"巴尔兹说,"他住在一幢孤零零的、又大又旧的房子里,一个朋友都没有,因为他脾

back, and he's horrid!'

'I don't believe you!' cried Mary. But the next day Basil's parents explained that she was going to live with her uncle in Yorkshire, in the north of England. Mary looked bored and cross and said nothing.

After the long sea journey, she was met in London by Mr Craven's housekeeper, Mrs Medlock. Together they travelled north by train. Mrs Medlock was a large woman, with a very red face and bright black eyes. Mary did not like her, but that was not surprising, because she did not usually like people. Mrs Medlock did not like Mary either.

'What a disagreeable child!' thought the housekeeper. 'But perhaps I should talk to her.'

'I can tell you a bit about your uncle if you like,' she said aloud. 'He lives in a big old house, a long way from anywhere. There are nearly a hundred rooms, but most of them are shut and locked. There's a big park round the house, and all kinds of gardens. Well, what do you think of that?'

'Nothing,' replied Mary. 'It doesn't matter to me.'

Mrs Medlock laughed. 'You're a hard little girl! Well, if *you* don't care, Mr Craven doesn't either. He never spends time on anyone. He's got a crooked back, you see, and although he's always been rich, he was never really happy until he married.'

'Married?' repeated Mary in surprise.

'Yes, he married a sweet, pretty girl, and he loved her

气太坏了。他还是个驼背,可怕极了!"

"我才不信呢!"玛丽大声说。可是第二天,巴兹尔的父母解释说她将要到英格兰北部的约克郡,跟她的舅舅住在一起。玛丽显得又烦躁又恼怒,可什么都没说。

轮船在海上航行了很久,克莱文先生的管家梅洛太太到伦敦来接玛丽,带她坐火车去北方。梅洛太太是个高大的女人,红脸膛,长着一双明亮的黑眼睛。玛丽不喜欢她,这也没什么好奇怪的,因为她通常谁也不喜欢。梅洛太太也不怎么喜欢玛丽。

"这孩子可真不讨人喜欢!"管家心里想,"不过也许我该跟她聊聊。"

"要是你愿意,我可以给你讲讲你舅舅的事。"她大声说。"他住在一幢很大的老宅子里,离哪儿都不近。那个宅子差不多有一百个房间,可大部分都紧闭着,上了锁。房子周围有一片很大的园林,还有各式的花园。你觉得怎么样?"

"不怎么样,"玛丽答道,"跟我一点关系都没有。"

梅洛太太笑了:"你这个小倔丫头!好啦,如果你不在乎,克莱文先生自然也不在乎。他从不把时间花在任何人身上,他是个驼背,而且,尽管一直都很有钱,在他结婚之前他从来没有真正快乐过。"

"结婚?"玛丽惊奇地重复道。

"是啊,娶了个温柔美丽的姑娘,他非常

Yorkshire *n. a former county of England.* 约克郡(英国一个郡)。**explain** *v. to tell someone something in a way that helps them understand it better.* 解释,说明。**housekeeper** *n. a person employed to manage a household.* 管家。

deeply. So when she died—'

'Oh! Did she die?' asked Mary, interested.

'Yes, she did. And now he doesn't care about anybody. If he's at home, he stays in his room and sees nobody. He won't want to see *you*, so you must stay out of his way and do what you're told.'

Mary stared out of the train window at the grey sky and the rain. She was not looking forward to life at her uncle's house.

The train journey lasted all day, and it was dark when they arrived at the station. Then there was a long drive to get to the house. It was a cold, windy night, and it was raining heavily. After a while Mary began to hear a strange, wild noise. She looked out of the window, but could see nothing except the darkness.

'What's that noise?' she asked Mrs Medlock. 'It's — It's not the sea, is it?'

'No, that's the moor. It's the sound the wind makes, blowing across the moor.'

'What is a moor?'

'It's just miles and miles of wild land, with no trees or houses. Your uncle's house is right on the edge of the moor.'

Mary listened to the strange, frightening sound. 'I don't like it,' she thought. 'I don't like it.' She looked more disagreeable than ever.

非常爱她。所以那姑娘一死——"

"哦！她死了吗？"玛丽感兴趣地问道。

"是啊，她死了。所以现在克莱文先生谁也不关心了，他在家的时候就待在屋子里谁也不见。他不会想见你的，所以你必须躲着他，照别人吩咐你的去做。"

玛丽望着车窗外灰色的天空和飘落的雨丝，对于住在舅舅家的生活没有一丝期盼。

火车走了一天，到站时天已经黑了。可离那幢房子还有很远的路，要搭马车才能到。这是一个寒冷的夜晚，风疾雨骤。过了一阵，玛丽听到一种奇怪的、狂野的声音，她向窗外看去，可除了黑暗什么都看不见。

"那是什么声音？"她问梅洛太太，"那——那不是海，对吗？"

"对，那不是海，是荒原的声音，是风吹过荒原时发出的声音。"

"荒原是什么？"

"就是大片大片的荒地，没有树，也没有房屋，你舅舅家就住在荒原的边上。"

玛丽听着那奇怪而又可怕的声音，心里想着："我讨厌它，我讨厌它。"她看上去更加不讨人喜欢了。

look forward to *hope*; *expect*. 盼望，期待。**moor** *n*. *a large area of high land covered with grass, bushes, with soil that is not good for growing crops*. 荒原。

13

2
Mary in Yorkshire

They arrived at a very large old house. It looked dark and unfriendly from the outside. Inside, Mary looked around the big shadowy hall, and felt very small and lost. They went straight upstairs. Mary was shown to a room where there was a warm fire and food on the table.

'This is your room,' said Mrs Medlock. 'Go to bed when you've had some supper. And remember, you must stay in your room! Mr Craven doesn't want you to wander all over the house!'

When Mary woke up the next morning, she saw a young servant girl cleaning the fireplace. The room seemed dark and rather strange, with pictures of dogs and horses and ladies on the walls. It was not a child's room at all. From the window she could not see any trees or houses, only wild land, which looked like a kind of purple sea.

'Who are you?' she asked the servant coldly.

'Martha, miss,' answered the girl with a smile.

'And what's that outside?' Mary continued.

'That's the moor,' smiled Martha. 'Do you like it?'

'No,' replied Mary immediately. 'I hate it.'

'That's because you don't know it. You *will* like it. I love it. It's lovely in spring and summer when there are flowers. It always smells so sweet. The air's so fresh, and the birds sing so

2 玛丽在约克郡的日子

她们来到一座很大的旧房子前,从外面看上去黑暗而冷漠。玛丽走进投满阴影的大厅,觉得自己非常渺小,不知身在何处。她们径直上了楼,玛丽被带进一个房间,里面生着火,很暖和,桌上摆着食物。

"这就是你的房间,"梅洛太太说,"吃点晚餐就睡吧。记住,你必须待在自己的房间里!克莱文先生可不想看见你在房子里到处乱逛!"

第二天一早玛丽醒来时,看见一个年轻的女仆正在清理壁炉。房间似乎很暗,相当古怪,墙上挂着狗、马还有女人的画像,一点也不像个孩子的房间。从窗子望出去,她看不到任何树或房屋,只有荒原,看上去像一片紫色的海。

"你是谁?"她冷冷地问那个仆人。

"我叫玛莎,小姐。"女孩笑着回答。

"外面是什么?"玛丽又问道。

"那是荒原,"玛莎笑着,"你喜欢吗?"

"不,"玛丽很快地答道,"我讨厌它。"

"那是因为你还不了解它。你会喜欢它的。我喜欢它。春天和夏天都开满了花,可爱极了,连空气都是甜的。那儿的空气新鲜

shadowy adj. hidden in darkness or shadows. 阴暗的。 **wander** v. travel without purpose. 闲逛,游荡。

15

beautifully. I never want to leave the moor.'

Mary was feeling very bad-tempered. 'You're a strange servant,' she said. 'In India we don't have conversations with servants. We give orders, and they obey, and that's that.'

Martha did not seem to mind Mary's crossness.

'I know I talk too much!' she laughed.

'Are you going to be *my* servant?' asked Mary.

'Well, not really. I work for Mrs Medlock. I'm going to clean your room and bring you your food, but you won't need a servant except for those things.'

'But who's going to dress me?'

Martha stopped cleaning, and stared at Mary.

'Tha' canna' dress thysen?' she asked, shocked.

'What do you mean? I don't understand your language!'

'Oh, I forgot. We all speak the Yorkshire dialect here, but of course you don't understand that. I meant to say, can't you put on your own clothes?'

'Of course not! My servant always used to dress me.'

'Well! I think you should learn to dress yourself. My mother always says people should be able to take care of themselves, even if they're rich and important.'

Little Miss Mary was furious with Martha. 'It's different in India where I come from! You don't know anything about India, or about servants, or about anything! You... you...' She could not explain what she meant. Suddenly she felt very confused and lonely. She threw herself down on the bed and start-

极了,鸟也叫得那么动听,我从来都不想离开它。"

玛丽感到很懊恼。"你可真怪,"她说,"在印度我们从来不跟用人交谈。我们下命令,他们服从,这就够了。"

玛莎对玛丽的小姐脾气好像并不在意。

"我知道我说得太多了!"她笑着说。

玛丽问道:"你会给我做用人吗?"

"嗯,也不全是。我为梅洛太太工作。我要打扫你的房间,给你拿吃的东西,可除此之外你并不需要一个用人。"

"那谁给我穿衣服呢?"

玛莎停下手里的活儿,瞪着玛丽。

"你自个儿不会穿衣服?"她惊讶地问。

"你是什么意思?我听不懂你的话!"

"噢,我忘了。我们这儿都说约克郡的方言,当然你是听不懂的。我是说,你自己不能穿衣服吗?"

"当然不能,总是用人给我穿的。"

"哈!我看你得学着自己穿衣服。我妈妈常说不管一个人多有钱,多尊贵,他都得能自己照顾自己。"

玛丽小姐有些生玛莎的气了。"我从印度来,我们那儿就不这样!你根本不知道印度,不知道用人,什么都不知道!你……你……"她没法表达清楚自己的意思。突然间觉得非常困惑,非常孤单,索性倒在床上大

shocked *adj. surprised.* 震惊的,吃惊的。**furious** *adj. angry.* 愤怒的。**confused** *adj. unable to understand something or think clearly about it.* 迷惑不解的。

ed crying wildly.

'Now, now, don't cry like that,' Martha said gently. 'I'm very sorry. You're right, I don't know anything about anything. Please stop crying, miss.'

She sounded kind and friendly, and Mary began to feel better and soon stopped crying. Martha went on talking as she finished her cleaning, but Mary looked out of the window in a bored way, and pretended not to listen.

'I've got eleven brothers and sisters, you know, miss. There's not much money in our house. And they all eat so much food! Mother says it's the good fresh air on the moor that makes them so hungry. My brother Dickon, he's always out on the moor. He's twelve, and he's got a horse which he rides sometimes.'

'Where did he get it?' asked Mary. She had always wanted an animal of her own, and so she began to feel a little interest in Dickon.

'Oh, it's a wild horse, but he's a kind boy, and animals like him, you see. Now you must have your breakfast, miss. Here it is on the table.'

'I don't want it,' said Mary. 'I'm not hungry.'

'What!' cried Martha. 'My little brothers and sisters would eat all this in five minutes!'

'Why?' asked Mary coldly.

'Because they don't get enough to eat, that's why, and they're always hungry. You're very lucky to have the food,

哭起来。

"好啦,好啦,别哭啦,"玛莎轻轻地说,"对不起,你是对的,我是什么也不知道。请你别哭了,小姐。"

她的声音和善而友好,玛丽感觉好了一些,很快止住了哭泣。玛莎打扫完继续说着话,可玛丽却无聊地望着窗外,假装根本不去听她讲话。

"你看,小姐,我家有 11 个兄弟姐妹,家里没什么钱,他们又都吃得那么多!我妈妈说是荒原上清新的空气让他们这么饿的。我弟弟狄肯总是在荒原上,他今年 12 岁,有一匹马,偶尔他会骑一骑。"

"他的马是从哪儿来的?"玛丽问。她一直都想有只属于自己的动物,因此开始对狄肯有了一点兴趣。

"哦,那是匹野马,可狄肯是个好孩子,动物都喜欢他。这会儿你该吃早餐了,就放在桌子上呢。"

"我不想吃,"玛丽说,"我不饿。"

"什么!"玛莎叫道,"我的弟弟妹妹们可要不了 5 分钟就能把它们都吃光!"

"为什么?"玛丽冷冷地问。

"因为他们没有足够的东西吃,就因为这个,他们总是觉得饿。你有饭吃可是很幸

miss. 'Mary said nothing, but she drank some tea and ate a little bread.

'Now put a coat on and run outside to play,' said Martha. 'It'll do you good to be in the fresh air.'

Mary looked out of the window at the cold grey sky. 'Why should I go out on a day like this?' she asked.

'Well, there's nothing to play with indoors, is there?'

Mary realized Martha was right. 'But who will go with me?' she said.

Martha stared at her. 'Nobody. You'll have to learn to play by yourself. Dickon plays by himself on the moors for hours, with the wild birds, and the sheep, and the other animals.' She looked away for a moment. 'Perhaps I shouldn't tell you this, but—but one of the walled gardens is locked up. Nobody's been in it for ten years. It was Mrs Craven's garden, and when she died so suddenly, Mr Craven locked it and buried the key — Oh, I must go, I can hear Mrs Medlock's bell ringing for me.'

Mary went downstairs and wandered through the great empty gardens. Many of the fruit and vegetable gardens had walls round them, but there were no locked doors. She saw an old man digging in one of the vegetable gardens, but he looked cross and unfriendly, so she walked on.

'How ugly it all looks in winter!' she thought. 'But what a mystery the locked garden is! Why did my uncle bury the key? If he loved his wife, why did he hate her garden? Perhaps I'll never know. I don't suppose I'll like him if I ever

运的,小姐。"玛丽什么也没说,不过她喝了点茶,还吃了点面包。

"好了,穿上外套跑到外面去玩儿吧,"玛莎说,"新鲜空气对你有好处。"

玛丽望了望窗外阴冷的灰色天空,问道,"这种天气干嘛要出去玩呢?"

"因为屋子里也没什么可玩的,对不对?"

玛丽觉得玛莎说得不错,又说:"可是谁跟我一块去呢?"

玛莎瞪着她:"没人会去。你得学会自己玩,狄肯一个人在荒原能玩上几个小时,他跟飞鸟、羊还有其他动物一起玩。"她把目光移开,停了一会儿,说道:"也许我不该告诉你这个,不过——不过有一座被墙围住的花园是上了锁的。有 10 年没人进去过了,那是克莱文太太的花园,她死得那么突然,克莱文先生就把它锁上了,还把钥匙也埋了起来——哦,我得走了,我听见梅洛太太在摇铃叫我呢。"

玛丽下了楼在空旷的大花园中闲逛。很多果园和菜园周围都有围墙,可没有锁上门的。她看见一个老人在其中一个菜园中挖地,不过他看上去脾气不好,也不和善,于是玛丽继续往前走。

"冬天一切看上去都那么丑!"她想,"可那座上了锁的花园多神秘啊!舅舅为什么要把钥匙埋起来呢?要是他爱他妻子,他干嘛那么讨厌她的花园呢?也许我永远也不会知道了。我看就是看到他我也不会喜欢

realize v. to gradually begin to understand something that you did not know or notice before. 意识到,认识到。**vegetable** n. a part of a plant used as food. 蔬菜。**dig** v. make a hole in earth or sand using your hands, a machine, or a tool. 挖,掘。**mystery** n. something that you are not able to understand, explain, or get information about. 神秘,秘密,谜。

21

meet him. And he won't like me, so I won't be able to ask him.'

Just then she noticed a robin singing to her from a tree on the other side of a wall. 'I think that tree's in the secret garden!' she told herself. 'There's an extra wall here, and there's no way in.'

She went back to where the gardener was digging, and spoke to him. At first he answered in a very bad-tempered way, but suddenly the robin flew down near them, and the old man began to smile. He looked a different person then, and Mary thought how much nicer people looked when they smiled. The gardener spoke gently to the robin, and the pretty little bird hopped on the ground near them.

'He's my friend, he is,' said the old man. 'There aren't any other robins in the garden, so he's a bit lonely.' He spoke in strong Yorkshire dialect, so Mary had to listen carefully to understand him.

She looked very hard at the robin. 'I'm lonely too,' she said. She had not realized this before.

'What's your name?' she asked the gardener.

'Ben Weatherstaff. I'm lonely myself. The robin's my only friend, you see.'

'I haven't got any friends at all,' said Mary.

Yorkshire people always say what they are thinking, and old Ben was a Yorkshire moor man. 'We're alike, you and me,' he told Mary. 'We're not pretty to look at, and we're both very

他,他也不会喜欢我的,所以我还是没法儿问他。"

正在这时,她看到一只知更鸟在一堵墙后面的树上冲她叫着。"我看那棵树就在秘密花园里!"她自言自语着,"这儿另外有一堵墙,而且没有进去的路。"

她回到园丁挖土的地方,跟他搭话。一开始他的回答很不耐烦,可是突然那只知更鸟飞到他们身旁,老人开始有了笑容。这会儿他看上去像换了个人。玛丽想,人微笑的时候看着就要好许多。园丁温和地跟知更鸟说话,而那漂亮的小鸟就在他们旁边的地上跳来跳去。

"他是我的朋友,是的,"老人说,"园子里没有别的知更鸟,所以它觉得有点孤独。"老人说话带着浓重的约克郡口音,所以玛丽得非常仔细才能听得懂他的话。

她紧紧盯着那只知更鸟,说:"我也很孤独。"在这之前她从没有意识到这一点。

"你叫什么名字?"她问园丁。

"本·威瑟斯塔夫。我自己一个人很孤独,瞧,这只知更鸟是我唯一的朋友。"

"可我什么朋友都没有。"玛丽说。

约克郡人从来都是心直口快,本这个老头正是约克郡荒原上的人。"你和我,咱俩差不多。"他对玛丽说,"长得丑,脾气还都不好。"

robin *n. a small brown European bird with a red chest.* 知更鸟。**gardener** *n. someone whose job is to take care of a garden.* 园丁。**dialect** *n. a way of speaking a language that is used only in a particular area or by a particular group.* 方言。

disagreeable.'

Nobody had ever said this to Mary before. 'Am I really as ugly and disagreeable as Ben?' she wondered.

Suddenly the robin flew to a tree near Mary and started singing to her. Ben laughed loudly.

'Well!' he said. 'He wants to be your friend!'

'Oh! Would you please be my friend?' she whispered to the robin. She spoke in a soft, quiet voice and old Ben looked at her in surprise.

'You said that really nicely!' he said. 'You sound like Dickon, when he talks to animals on the moor.'

'Do you know Dickon?' asked Mary. But just then the robin flew away. 'Oh look, he's flown into the garden with no door! Please, Ben, how can I get into it?'

Ben stopped smiling and picked up his spade. 'You can't, and that's that. It's not your business. Nobody can find the door. Run away and play, will you? I must get on with my work.' And he walked away. He did not even say goodbye.

In the next few days Mary spent almost all her time in the gardens. The fresh air from the moor made her hungry, and she was becoming stronger and healthier. One day she noticed the robin again. He was on top of a wall, singing to her. 'Good morning! Isn't this fun! Come this way!' he seemed to say, as he hopped along the wall. Mary began to laugh as she danced along beside him. 'I know the secret garden's on the other side of this wall!' she thought excitedly. 'And the robin

以前从来没有人对玛丽说过这些。她有些怀疑："我真是像本一样又丑又不招人喜欢吗？"

突然，知更鸟飞到玛丽近旁的一棵树上，开始对着她唱歌。本大声笑起来。

"看哪！"他说，"他想做你的朋友呢！"

"哦！你愿意做我的朋友吗？"她小声地对知更鸟说。她的声音又轻又柔，本老头惊奇地望着她。

"你说得真好！"他说，"听起来像狄肯，他在荒原上跟动物说话时就是这样。"

"你认识狄肯吗？"玛丽问道。但就在这时知更鸟飞走了。"哦，看哪，他飞到那个没有门的花园里去了！本，请问，我怎么才能进去呢？"

本收起了笑容，拾起他的铲子。"你不能进去，就是不行。那不是你的事儿，没人能找到那扇门。到别的地方去玩吧，好吗？我得接着干活儿了。"然后他就走开了，甚至连再见也没说。

以后的几天，玛丽几乎所有的时间都待在花园里。荒原上吹来的新鲜空气让她感到饥饿，而她也变得强壮，变得健康了。一天，她又看见了知更鸟。他在一堵墙的顶上冲她唱歌。他好像是在说："早上好！多好玩啊！上这儿来！"一边沿着围墙跳着。玛丽一边跟在他旁边跳着，一边放声笑起来。"我知道秘密花园在这堵墙的那一边！"她兴奋地想着，"知更鸟就住在那

whisper *v. say something very quietly so that other people cannot hear you.* 低声说。**get on with** *go on with.* 继续。**spade** *n. a tool used for digging earth.* 铲子。

lives there! But where's the door?'

That evening she asked Martha to stay and talk to her beside the fire after supper. They could hear the wind blowing round the old house, but the room was warm and comfortable. Mary only had one idea in her head.

'Tell me about the secret garden,' she said.

'Well, all right then, miss, but we aren't supposed to talk about it, you know. It was Mrs Craven's favourite garden, and she and Mr Craven used to take care of it themselves. They spent hours there, reading and talking. Very happy, they were. They used the branch of an old tree as a seat. But one day when she was sitting on the branch, it broke, and she fell. She was very badly hurt and the next day she died. That's why he hates the garden so much, and won't let anyone go in there.'

'How sad!' said Mary. 'Poor Mr Craven!' It was the first time that she had ever felt sorry for anyone.

Just then, as she was listening to the wind outside, she heard another noise, in the house.

'Can you hear a child crying?' she asked Martha.

Martha looked confused. 'Er — no,' she replied. 'No, I think...it must be the wind.'

But at that moment the wind blew open their door and they heard the crying very clearly.

'I told you!' cried Mary.

At once Martha shut the door. 'It was the wind,' she repeated. But she did not speak in her usual natural way, and

儿！可是门在哪儿呢?"

那天晚饭后她让玛莎留下,在壁炉边上陪她说话。她们听到风在房子周围盘旋,而屋子里又暖和又舒适。玛丽的脑子里只有一个念头。

"给我讲讲那个秘密花园吧。"她说。

"嗯,那好吧,小姐,不过你知道我们是不许谈论它的。那是克莱文夫人最喜欢的花园,她和克莱文先生曾亲自打理它。他们时常在里面待上几个小时,读书,谈心,他们非常幸福。他们拿一根老树的枝当座椅。可是有一天,当克莱文夫人坐在上面时,树枝断了,她摔下来,伤得很重,第二天就死了。这就是为什么克莱文先生那么讨厌那个花园,而且不让任何人进去的原因。"

"太惨了!"玛丽说,"可怜的克莱文先生!"这是玛丽第一次为别人感到难过。

就在这时,当她倾听着外面的风时,她听到了另一个声音,就在这房子里面。

"你听到小孩在哭吗?"她问玛莎。

玛莎看上去很慌乱,"嗯——没有,"她答道,"不,我想——肯定是风。"

可是这时风把她们的门吹开了。她们真切地听到了哭声。

"我说的没错吧!"玛丽大声说。

玛莎立刻把门关上,还是说:"那就是风声。"可她的声音不像平时那么自然,所以玛

comfortable *adj*. *at ease; feeling pleasant*. 舒服的, 安乐的。**branch** *n*. *a part of a tree that grows out of its trunk with leaves, flowers, or fruit growing on it*. 树枝。

27

Mary did not believe her.

The next day it was very rainy, so Mary did not go out. Instead she decided to wander round the house, looking into some of the hundred rooms that Mrs Medlock had told her about. She spent all morning going in and out of dark, silent rooms, which were full of heavy furniture and old pictures. She saw no servants at all, and was on her way back to her room for lunch, when she heard a cry. 'It's a bit like the cry that I heard last night!' she thought. Just then the housekeeper, Mrs Medlock, appeared, with her keys in her hand.

'What are you doing here?' she asked crossly.

'I didn't know which way to go, and I heard someone crying,' answered Mary.

'You didn't hear anything! Go back to your room now. And if you don't stay there, I'll lock you in!'

Mary hated Mrs Medlock for this. 'There *was* someone crying, I know there was!' she said to herself. 'But I'll discover who it is soon!' She was almost beginning to enjoy herself in Yorkshire.

丽根本不相信她。

第二天雨下得很大,玛丽没有出去,而是打定主意在房子里转转,看看梅洛太太讲过的那上百个房间。她整个上午都在出入那些昏暗寂静的房间,房间里满是笨重的家具和古旧的画。她没看到一个用人,当她转身回房间吃午饭时,听到有人哭泣的声音。她想:"听起来有点像昨天晚上的哭声。"就在这时管家梅洛太太出现了,手里拎着大串钥匙。

"你在这里干什么?"她生气地问道。

"我不知道该从哪儿出去,我听见有人在哭。"玛丽回答。

"你什么也没听见!现在就回你的房间去,你要是不待在那儿,我就把你锁起来!"

玛丽不喜欢梅洛太太这种样子:"就是有人在哭嘛,我知道肯定有!"她自言自语道:"不过我会很快弄清楚是谁的!"她几乎开始喜欢在约克郡的生活了。

furniture *n*. *the movable articles in a room that make it fit for living or working*. 家具。**appear** *v*. *become visible*. 出现。**disappear** *v*. *pass out of sight*. 失踪。**discover** *v*. *find someone or something that was missing or hidden*. 发现。

3
Finding the secret garden

When Mary woke up two days later, the wind and rain had all disappeared, and the sky was a beautiful blue. 'Spring'll be here soon,' said Martha happily. 'You'll love the moor then, when it's full of flowers and birds.'

'Could I get to the moor?' asked Mary.

'You've never done much walking, have you? I don't think you could walk the five miles to our cottage!'

'But I'd like to meet your family,' Mary said.

Martha looked at the little girl for a moment. She remembered how disagreeable Mary had been when she first arrived. But now, Mary looked interested and friendly.

'I'll ask Mother,' said Martha. 'She can always think of a good plan. She's sensible and hardworking and kind — I know you'll like her.'

'I like Dickon, although I've never seen him.'

'I wonder what Dickon will think of you?'

'He won't like me,' said Mary. 'No one does.'

'But do you like yourself? That's what Mother would ask.'

'No, not really. I've never thought of that.'

'Well, I must go now. It's my day off, so I'm going home to help Mother with the housework. Goodbye, miss. See you tomorrow.'

3　　找到秘密花园

　　两天后,当玛丽早上醒来时,风住了,雨也停了,天空是一片美丽的蓝色。"春天就要来了!"玛莎快活地说道,"那时到处是花儿和小鸟,你会喜欢荒原的。"

　　"我能去荒原吗?"玛丽问。

　　"你没有走过那么远的路吧,对不对?我看你走不了5里路到我们住的小屋去!"

　　"可是我想见一见你的家人。"玛丽说。

　　玛莎对着这个小女孩注视了片刻,她想起玛丽刚来这儿时是多么地不讨人喜欢,可是现在,她看上去兴致勃勃的,也很友好。

　　"我得问问妈妈,"玛莎说,"她总能想出好办法的。她聪明、能干,还很善良,我想你会喜欢她的。"

　　"我喜欢狄肯,虽然我没见过他。"

　　"我不知道狄肯会不会喜欢你。"

　　"他不会喜欢我的,"玛丽说,"没人喜欢我。"

　　"但是你喜欢自己吗?妈妈会这么问的。"

　　"不,不太喜欢,我从来没想过这个问题。"

　　"哦,我得走了,今天是我休息的日子,我得回家帮妈妈做家务。再见,小姐,明天见。"

cottage *n. a small house, usually in a village or the countryside.* 小木屋,农舍。**sensible** *adj. reasonable and practical.* 通情达理的。**housework** *n. the work that you do to keep your house clean and neat.* 家务。

Mary felt lonelier than ever when Martha had gone, so she went outside. The sunshine made the gardens look different. And the change in the weather had even made Ben Weatherstaff easier to talk to.

'Can you smell spring in the air?' he asked her. 'Things are growing, deep down in the ground. Soon you'll see little green shoots coming up—young plants, they are. You watch them.'

'I will,' replied Mary. 'Oh, there's the robin!' The little bird hopped on to Ben's spade. 'Are things growing in the garden where he lives?'

'What garden?' said Ben, in his bad-tempered voice.

'You know, the secret garden. Are the flowers dead there?' She really wanted to know the answer.

'Ask the robin,' said Ben crossly. 'He's the only one who's been in there for the last ten years.'

Ten years was a long time, Mary thought. She had been born ten years ago. She walked away, thinking. She had begun to like the gardens, and the robin, and Martha and Dickon and their mother. Before she came to Yorkshire, she had not liked anybody.

She was walking beside the long wall of the secret garden, when a most wonderful thing happened. She suddenly realized the robin was following her. She felt very pleased and excited by this, and cried out, 'You like me, don't you? And I like you too!' As he hopped along beside her, she hopped and sang too, to show him that she was his friend. Just then he stopped

玛莎走后,玛丽觉得更孤单了,于是她走到外面。阳光使花园看上去与往日不同,而且天气的变化似乎让本·威瑟斯塔夫也变得喜欢说话了。

　　"你能闻到春天的气息吗?"他问玛丽,"在深深的泥土下面,万物在生长。很快你就会看见绿色的嫩芽长出来——那些幼苗,你会看见它们的。"

　　"我会的,"玛丽答道,"噢! 知更鸟!"小鸟蹦到了本的铲子上。"它住的园子里一切也在生长吗?"

　　"什么园子?"本问道,语气中有些暴躁。

　　"你知道的,那个秘密花园。那儿的花儿死了吗?"她是真的想知道答案。

　　"问知更鸟吧,"本不耐烦地说,"它是唯一在这 10 年里去过那儿的。"

　　10 年是段很长的时间,玛丽想。她是10 年前出生的。她走开了,想着心事。她已经开始喜欢上园子、知更鸟、玛莎、狄肯,还有他们的母亲。在她来约克郡之前,她从来也没喜欢过谁。

　　她正在秘密花园长长的围墙外走着,一件惊人的事情发生了。她突然发现知更鸟在跟着她,她感到非常高兴,非常激动,她叫道:"你喜欢我,对吗? 我也喜欢你!"知更鸟一蹦一跳地在她左右,她也一样跳着唱着,告诉知更鸟她是他的朋友。这时知更鸟

shoot *n. a very young plant , or a new part growing on a plant.* 新芽,嫩枝。**hop** *v. jump.* 跳,蹦。

at a place where a dog had dug a hole in the ground. As Mary looked at the hole, she noticed something almost buried there. She put her hand in and pulled it out. It was an old key.

'Perhaps it's been buried for ten years,' she whispered to herself. 'Perhaps it's the key to the secret garden!'

She looked at it for a long time. How lovely it would be to find the garden, and see what had happened to it in the last ten years! She could play in it all by herself, and nobody would know she was there. She put the key safely in her pocket.

The next morning Martha was back at Misselthwaite Manor, and told Mary all about her day with her family.

'I really enjoyed myself. I helped Mother with the whole week's washing and baking. And I told the children about you. They wanted to know about your servants, and the ship that brought you to England, and everything!'

'I can tell you some more for next time,' offered Mary. 'They'd like to hear about riding on elephants and camels, wouldn't they?'

'Oh, that would be kind of you, miss! And look, Mother has sent you a present!'

'A present!' repeated Mary. How could a family of fourteen hungry people give anyone a present!

'Mother bought it from a man who came to the door to sell things. She told me, "Martha, you've brought me your pay, like a good girl, and we need it all, but I'm going to buy something for that lonely child at the Manor," and she bought one, and

在一个地方停下来,那儿的地上有一个狗挖出来的洞。玛丽往洞里看时,发现有个东西埋在里面,她伸手进去拣出来,是一把旧钥匙。

"说不定它已经被埋了10年了,"她低声地自言自语道,"说不定这就是秘密花园的钥匙!"

她拿着钥匙看了很久。要是能找到秘密花园,看看这10年间都发生了些什么变化,那该有多棒啊!她就能一个人在里面玩儿,谁也不知道她会在那儿。她把钥匙小心地放进口袋里。

第二天早晨,玛莎回到米瑟斯韦特庄园,她给玛丽讲述了她同家人共度的一天中的情况。

"我真高兴,我帮妈妈把一个星期要洗的东西都洗了,还烤了一个星期要吃的面包。我对孩子们讲起你,他们都想知道你在印度的仆人们,带你来英国的大船,一切的事情!"

"下次我会多讲些给你听,"玛丽说,"他们会喜欢听骑大象和骑骆驼的事,对吗?"

"噢,小姐,你真是太好了!对了,看,妈妈送给你的礼物!"

"礼物!"玛丽重复道。一个有着14个挨饿的人的家庭怎么能给人送礼物!

"妈妈从上门卖货的人那儿买的。她告诉我说:'玛莎,你是个好孩子,把工钱都给了我,我们需要用钱,不过我要给庄园里那个孤单的孩子买点东西。'于是她就买了一个,瞧,就在这儿!"

elephant n. a very large wild animal that has thick gray skin and a very long nose. 大象。**camel** n. a large animal with a long neck and one or two humps on its back. 骆驼。**present** n. gift. 礼物。

here it is!'

It was a skipping-rope. Mary stared at it.

'What is it?' she asked.

'Don't they have skipping-ropes in India? Well, this is how you use it. Just watch me.'

Martha took the rope and ran into the middle of the room. She counted up to a hundred as she skipped.

'That looks lovely,' said Mary. 'Your mother is very kind. Do you think I could ever skip like that?'

'Just try,' said Martha. 'Mother says it'll make you strong and healthy. Skip outside in the fresh air.'

Mary put her coat on and took the skipping-rope. As she was opening the door, she thought of something and turned round.

'Martha, it was your money really. Thank you.' She never thanked people usually and she did not know how to do it. So she held out her hand, because she knew that adults did that.

Martha shook her hand and laughed. 'You're a strange child,' she said. 'Like an old woman! Now run away and play!'

The skipping-rope was wonderful. Mary counted and skipped, skipped and counted, until her face was hot and red. She was having more fun than she had ever had before. She skipped through the gardens until she found Ben Weatherstaff, who was digging and talking to his robin. She wanted them both to see her skip.

'Well!' said Ben. 'You're looking fine and healthy today!

那是一根跳绳。玛丽瞪大眼睛望着它。

"这是什么?"她问。

"在印度没有人跳绳吗? 好吧,你得这么用,看着我。"

玛莎拿着绳子跑到房间中央,跳了有100下。

"真好看,"玛丽说道,"你妈妈真好,你觉得我能跳得那么好吗?"

"试试看,"玛莎说,"妈妈说它会让你健康又强壮。要在外面新鲜空气中跳。"

玛丽穿上大衣,拿起跳绳,要去开门的时候她好像想起了什么,又转回来。

"玛莎,这其实是花你的钱,谢谢你。"她平常从来不去感谢别人,也不知道该怎么做。于是她伸出手,因为她知道大人们都那么做。

玛莎握住她的手笑起来,说:"你可真是个怪孩子,像个老太婆! 现在就到外面玩去吧!"

跳绳真棒,玛丽跳着数着,数着跳着,跳得脸蛋儿又红又热,她从来没有这么快活过。她跳过花园,找到本·威瑟斯塔夫,老人正在挖土,一边跟知更鸟说着话。她想让他们俩都看她跳绳。

"哈!你今天看上去不错,很健康,接着

skipping-rope *n. a length of rope revolved over the head and under the feet while jumping as a game or exercise.* 跳绳。**adult** *n. someone who is no longer a child and is legally responsible for their actions.* 大人,成年人。

Go on skipping. It's good for you.'

Mary skipped all the way to the secret garden wall. And there was the robin! He had followed her! Mary was very pleased.

'You showed me where the key was yesterday,' she laughed. 'I've got it in my pocket. So you ought to show me the door today!'

The robin hopped on to an old climbing plant on the wall, and sang his most beautiful song. Suddenly the wind made the plant move, and Mary saw something under the dark green leaves. The thick, heavy plant was covering a door. Mary's heart was beating fast and her hands were shaking as she pushed the leaves away and found the keyhole. She took the key out of her pocket, and it fitted the hole. Using both hands, she managed to unlock the door. Then she turned round to see if anyone was watching. But there was no one, so she pushed the door, which opened, slowly, for the first time in ten years. She walked quickly in and shut the door behind her. At last she was inside the secret garden!

It was the loveliest, most exciting place she had ever seen. There were old rose trees everywhere, and the walls were covered with climbing roses. She looked carefully at the grey branches. Were the roses still alive? Ben would know. She hoped they weren't all dead. But she was *inside* the wonderful garden, in a world of her own. It seemed very strange and silent, but she did not feel lonely at all. Then she noticed some

玛莎关上门出去了,玛丽独自想着:"这可是人们住过的最奇怪的房子了。"

4

Meeting Dickon

Mary spent nearly a week working in the secret garden.
Each day she found new shoots coming out of the
ground. Soon, there would be flowers everywhere — thousands
of them. It was an exciting game to her. When she was inside
those beautiful old walls, no one knew where she was.

During that week she became more friendly with Ben, who
was often digging in one of the vegetable gardens.

'What are your favourite flowers, Ben?' she asked him one
day.

'Roses. I used to work for a young lady who loved roses, you
see, and she had a lot in her garden. That was ten years ago.
But she died. Very sad, it was.'

'What happened to the roses?' asked Mary.

'They were left there, in the garden.'

'If rose branches look dry and grey, are they still alive?'
asked Mary. It was so important to know!

'In the spring they'll show green shoots, and then — But
why are you so interested in roses?' he asked.

Mary's face went red. 'I just... wanted to pretend I've got a
garden. I haven't got anyone to play with.'

'Well, that's true,' said Ben. He seemed to feel sorry for
her. Mary decided she liked old Ben, although he was sometimes bad-tempered.

4 见到狄肯

玛丽花了将近一个星期的时间在秘密花园里干活儿。每天,她都看到新的嫩芽从土里冒出来,很快,到处都将开满成千上万的花朵。对她来说,这是一个让她兴奋不已的游戏。她一走进那些美丽的旧围墙,就没人知道她去了哪儿。

那个星期她开始对经常不停地在那块菜地里挖土的本更加友好了。

一天,她问他:"本,你最喜欢什么花?"

"玫瑰。我曾经给一位喜爱玫瑰的年轻女士干活儿,她的花园里有好多玫瑰,那都是10年前的事了。可是她死了,很惨。"

"那些玫瑰怎么样了?"玛丽问。

"它们就留在花园里了。"

"要是玫瑰的枝子看上去又干又暗,它们还活着吗?"玛丽问道。弄懂这个简直是太重要了!

"到了春天它们就会长出绿色的嫩芽,然后——你怎么会对玫瑰这么有兴趣呢?"他问。

玛丽的脸红了。"我只是——设想自己有个花园,没人跟我一起玩儿。"

"嗯,那倒是真的,"本说。他似乎是在为她感到难过。玛丽决定喜欢本,尽管他有时脾气不大好。

spend *v.* *use time, effort, or energy to do something.* 花费(时间,金钱)。

She skipped along and into the wood at the end of the gardens. Suddenly she heard a strange noise, and there in front of her was a boy. He was sitting under a tree, playing on a wooden pipe. He was about twelve, with a healthy red face and bright blue eyes. There was a squirrel and a crow in the tree, and two rabbits sitting on the grass near him.

'They're listening to the music!' thought Mary. 'I mustn't frighten them!' She stood very still.

The boy stopped playing. 'That's right,' he said. 'Animals don't like it if you move suddenly. I'm Dickon and you must be Miss Mary. I've brought you the spade and the seeds.'

He spoke in an easy, friendly way. Mary liked him at once. As they were looking at the seed packets together, the robin hopped on to a branch near them. Dickon listened carefully to the robin's song.

'He's saying he's your friend,' he told Mary.

'Really? Oh, I am pleased he likes me. Can you understand everything that birds say?'

'I think I do, and they think I do. I've lived on the moor with them for so long. Sometimes I think I *am* a bird or an animal, not a boy at all!' His smile was the widest she had ever seen.

He explained how to plant the seeds. Suddenly he said, 'I can help you plant them! Where's your garden?'

Mary went red, then white. She had never thought of this. What was she going to say?

她蹦跳着来到花园尽头的树丛中,突然,她听到一个陌生的声音,有个男孩出现在她的面前。他正坐在一棵树下,吹着一根木管。他大约十二岁,脸色健康、红润,有一双明亮的蓝眼睛。树上有一只松鼠,还有只乌鸦,他身边的草地上还有两只小兔子。

玛丽想:"它们都在听音乐,我可别吓着它们!"她静静地站着。

男孩停下来,说:"这就对了,动物们不喜欢你唐突的动作。我是狄肯,你肯定就是玛丽小姐了。我给你带铲子和花籽来了。"

他说话的样子轻松友善,玛丽一下子就喜欢上他了。他们一起看装着花籽的小包时,知更鸟蹦到了旁边的树枝上,狄肯仔细听着知更鸟的歌声。

他告诉玛丽说:"它说它是你的朋友。"

"真的吗?哦,它喜欢我,我真太高兴了。你能听懂鸟说的每一句话吗?"

"我觉得是,它们也这么想。我跟它们一起在荒原上住了这么久,有时候我觉得自己就是一只鸟或是一只动物,根本就不是个孩子!"玛丽从来没有见过像他这样开心的笑容。

他讲解着该怎么种那些花籽,突然他说:"我可以帮你种!你的花园在哪儿?"

玛丽脸红了,然后又变得苍白。她从没想到这一点,她该怎么说呢?

pipe *n. a simple musical instrument consisting of one or more tubes that you blow through.* 管,管乐器,笛子,箫。 **squirrel** *n. a gray or red-brown animal with a long thick tail that lives in trees.* 松鼠。 **crow** *n. a large black bird that makes a loud sound.* 乌鸦。 **rabbit** *n. a small animal with long ears and soft fur.* 兔子。

'Could you keep a secret? It's a great secret. If anyone dis-
covers it, I'll...I'll die!'

'I keep secrets for all the wild birds and animals on the
moor. So I can keep yours too,' he replied.

'I've stolen a garden,' she said very fast. 'Nobody goes into
it, nobody wants it. I love it and nobody takes care of it!
They're letting it die!' And she threw her arms over her face
and started crying.

'Don't cry,' said Dickon gently. 'Where is it?'

'Come with me and I'll show you,' said Miss Mary.

They went to the secret garden and entered it together.
Dickon walked round, looking at everything.

'Martha told me about this place, but I never thought I'd
see it,' he said. 'It's wonderful!'

'What about the roses?' asked Mary worriedly. 'Are they
still alive? What do you think?'

'Look at these shoots on the branches. Most of them are
alive all right.' He took out his knife and cut away some of the
dead wood from the rose trees. Mary showed him the work she
had done in the garden, and they talked as they cut and
cleared.

'Dickon,' said Mary suddenly, 'I like you. I never thought
I'd like as many as five people!'

'Only five!' laughed Dickon.

He did look funny when he laughed, thought Mary.

'Yes, your mother, Martha, the robin, Ben, and you.' Then

"你能保守秘密吗？这可是个大秘密。要是被人发现了，我就……我就得死！"

狄肯回答："我为荒原上所有的鸟兽保密，所以我也能为你保密。"

"我偷了一个花园，"她说得很快。"谁都没进去过，谁也不想要它。我喜欢它，可是没人照看它，他们就由着它死掉！"她把脸埋在臂弯里，哭了起来。

狄肯轻轻地说："别哭了，它在哪儿呢？"

"你跟我来，我让你看看它。"玛丽说。

他们来到秘密花园，一起走了进去。狄肯四处走着，每样东西都看看。

"玛莎跟我说过这个地方，可我从没想到能见到它，"他说，"它可太棒了！"

"那些玫瑰怎么样？"玛丽担心地问道，"它们还活着吗？你觉得呢？"

"看看枝子上的这些嫩芽，大部分已经活了。"他掏出小刀割去一些玫瑰树上已经枯死的枝条。玛丽给他看了自己在花园里干的活儿。他们一边修剪枝条，清理残叶，一边说着话。

"狄肯，"玛丽突然说道，"我喜欢你。我从没想到能喜欢 5 个人！"

"才 5 个人！"狄肯笑了。

他笑的样子很滑稽，玛丽心里想。

"是的，你妈妈、玛莎、知更鸟、本和你。"

reply *v. answer.* 回答。
steal *v. to take something that belongs to someone else without permission.* 偷。
worriedly *adv. anxiously.* 忧心忡忡地，为难地。

she asked him a question in Yorkshire dialect, because that was his language.

'Does tha' like me?' was her question.

'Of course! I likes thee wonderful!' replied Dickon, a big smile on his round face. Mary had never been so happy.

When she went back to the house for her lunch, she told Martha about Dickon's visit.

'I've got news for you too,' said Martha. 'Mr Craven's come home, and wants to see you! He's going away again to-morrow, for several months.'

'Oh!' said Mary. That was good news. She would have all summer in the secret garden before he came back. But she must be careful. He mustn't guess her secret now.

Just then Mrs Medlock arrived, in her best black dress, to take Mary down to Mr Craven's room.

Mary's uncle had black hair with some white in it, and high, crooked shoulders. His face was not ugly, but very sad. During their conversation he watched her in a worried way. Perhaps he was thinking of other things at the same time.

He looked at the thin child. 'Are you well?' he asked. Mary tried to keep her voice calm as she replied,

'I'm getting stronger and healthier.'

'What do you want to do, in this big empty house?'

'I. . . I just want to play outside — I enjoy that.'

'Yes, Martha's mother, Susan Sowerby, spoke to me the other day. She's a sensible woman — and she said you needed

然后她用约克郡的方言问了他一个问题,因为他就讲这种话。

她的问题是:"你喜欢我吗?"

"当然!我很喜欢你!"狄肯回答,圆圆的脸上露出灿烂的笑容。玛丽从来没有这么开心过。

回去吃午饭时,她告诉玛莎狄肯来过了。

"我也有事要告诉你,"玛莎说。"克莱文先生回来了,而且要见你!他明天又要走了,要走几个月呢。"

"哦!"玛丽说。那可是好消息。在他回来之前,她可以整个夏天都待在秘密花园里。不过她一定要小心,可不能让他这会儿就猜出她的秘密。

这时,梅洛太太进来了。她穿上了她最好的黑色长裙,带玛丽下楼到克莱文先生的房间。

玛丽的舅舅黑发中夹着银丝,高高的个子,背有些驼。他长得并不丑,但脸色阴沉。谈话中他神色忧郁地看着她,也许他同时在想着什么别的事情。

他看着这个瘦弱的孩子,问道:"你好吗?"玛丽在回答时尽量使自己的声音保持平静。

"我越来越结实、健康了。"

"在这样一座空荡荡的大房子里,你想做些什么呢?"

"我……我只是想在外面玩——我喜欢那样。"

"是啊,玛莎的母亲,苏珊·索尔比那天也对我这么说。她是个聪明人——她说你

Does tha'like me? = Do you like me?; I likes thee wonderful! = I like you very much! 约克郡方言。shoulder *n. one of the two parts of your body between your neck and the top of your arms.* 肩膀。conversation *n. chat, talk.* 谈话,交谈。

fresh air. But where do you play?'

'Everywhere! I just skip and run — and look for green shoots. I don't damage anything!'

'Don't look so frightened! Of course a child like you couldn't damage anything. Play where you like. Is there anything that you want?'

Mary came a step nearer to him, and her voice shook a little as she spoke. 'Could I — could I have a bit of garden?'

Mr Craven looked very surprised.

'To plant seeds in . . . to make them come alive!' Mary went on bravely. 'It was too hot in India, so I was always ill and tired there. But here it's different. I . . . I love the garden!'

He passed a hand quickly over his eyes. Then he looked kindly at Mary. 'I knew someone once who loved growing things, like you. Yes, child, take as much of the garden as you want.' He smiled gently at her. 'Now leave me. I'm very tired.'

Mary ran all the way back to her room.

'Martha!' she shouted. 'Mr Craven's really a nice man, but he looks very unhappy. He said I can have my own garden!'

She was planning to work in the garden with Dickon every day, to make it beautiful for the summer.

需要新鲜空气。可你都在哪儿玩呢?"

"哪儿都玩!我就是跳跳绳,跑来跑去——找那些绿色的嫩芽。我什么也没弄坏!"

"别这么害怕!像你这样的孩子当然什么也弄不坏。喜欢哪儿就在哪儿玩儿吧。你想要什么东西吗?"

玛丽往他身边走了一步,说话时声音有点发抖:"我能——我能有一小块花园吗?"

克莱文先生显得很惊讶。

"用来播种子,让它们长起来!"玛丽壮着胆子接着说道,"在印度天气太热了,所以我老是生病,老是觉得累。可这儿就不一样。我……我喜欢花园!"

克莱文先生很快地用一只手挡在眼睛前面,然后他和蔼地看着玛丽:"我曾经认识一个人,也喜欢种东西,像你一样。好吧,孩子,花园你想要多大都成。现在你可以走了,我很累了。"他和善地对她笑着。

玛丽一路小跑回到了自己的房间。

"玛莎!"她喊道,"克莱文先生真是个好人,可他看上去很不开心。他说我能有自己的花园!"

她打算每天与狄肯一起在花园里干活儿,让花园在夏天漂亮起来。

damage *v. to harm something physically so that it is broken, spoiled, or injured.* 毁坏,弄坏。
bravely *adv. dealing with danger or pain, without seeming to be frightened.* 勇敢地。

5
Meeting Colin

In the middle of the night Mary woke up. Heavy rain had started falling again, and the wind was blowing violently round the walls of the old house. Suddenly she heard crying again. This time she decided to discover who it was. She left her room, and in the darkness followed the crying sound, round corners and through doors, up and down stairs, to the other side of the big house. At last she found the right room. She pushed the door open and went in.

It was a big room with beautiful old furniture and pictures. In the large bed was a boy, who looked tired and cross, with a thin, white, tearful face. He stared at Mary.

'Who are you?' he whispered. 'Are you a dream?'

'No, I'm not. I'm Mary Lennox. Mr Craven's my uncle.'

'He's my father,' said the boy. 'I'm Colin Craven.'

'No one ever told me he had a son!' said Mary, very surprised.

'Well, no one ever told me you'd come to live here. I'm ill, you see. I don't want people to see me and talk about me. If I live, I may have a crooked back like my father, but I'll probably die.'

'What a strange house this is!' said Mary. 'So many secrets! Does your father come and see you often?'

54

5　见到柯林

　　半夜的时候,玛丽醒了。天又开始下大雨了,狂风在房子围墙周围猛烈地刮着。突然,她又听见了哭声,这次她决定要搞清楚那个人是谁。她走出房间,在黑暗中循着哭泣的声音,绕过墙角,穿过一扇扇门,上下楼梯,来到这所大房子的另一侧。终于她找到了那个房间,推开门,走了进去。

　　那是个很大的房间,摆着古旧的家具和画,非常漂亮。在一张大床上躺着一个男孩,看上去疲惫、烦躁。他的脸颊消瘦、苍白,挂满了泪痕。他瞪大眼睛看着玛丽。

　　“你是谁?”他小声问。“我是在做梦吧?”

　　“不,不是。我是玛丽·莲诺丝。克莱文先生是我舅舅。”

　　“他是我父亲,”那个男孩说道。“我叫柯林·克莱文。”

　　“从来没有人告诉过我他有个儿子!”玛丽说,觉得十分吃惊。

　　“嗯,也没人告诉我你在这儿住。你看到了,我病了。我不想让人们看见我议论我,要是我活下来,我可能会像父亲一样成为驼背,但是我可能会死的。”

　　“这所房子真是奇怪啊!”玛丽说,“这么多秘密! 你父亲常来看你吗?”

violently *adv. in a way that involves violence.* 粗暴地,激烈地。**probably** *adv. maybe, perhaps.* 可能,也许。

55

'Not often. He doesn't like seeing me because it makes him remember my mother. She died when I was born, so he almost hates me, I think.'

'Why do you say you're going to die?' asked Mary.

'I've always been ill. I've nearly died several times, and my back's never been strong. My doctor feels sure that I'm going to die. But he's my father's cousin, and very poor, so he'd like me to die. Then he'd get all the money when my father dies. He gives me medicine and tells me to rest. We had a grand doctor from London once, who told me to go out in the fresh air and try to get well. But I hate fresh air. And another thing, all the servants have to do what I want, because if I'm angry, I become ill.'

Mary thought she liked this boy, although he seemed so strange. He asked her lots of questions, and she told him all about her life in India.

'How old are you?' he asked suddenly.

'I'm ten, and so are you,' replied Mary, forgetting to be careful, 'because when you were born the garden door was locked and the key was buried. And I know that was ten years ago.'

Colin sat up in bed and looked very interested. 'What door? Who locked it? Where's the key? I want to see it. I'll make the servants tell me where it is. They'll take me there and you can come too.'

'Oh, please! Don't—don't do that!' cried Mary.

"不常来。他不喜欢见到我,因为这让他想起妈妈。她是生我的时候死的,所以他八成是恨我,我这么想。"

"你为什么说自己会死呢?"玛丽问。

"我一直在生病。我已经死过几次了,而且我的脊背向来就很弱。我的医生肯定我会死的。他是我父亲的表弟,而且很穷,所以他巴不得我死呢。那样等我父亲去世以后,所有的钱就都归他了。他给我药吃,让我休息,有一回我们从伦敦请了个有名的大夫,他让我到外面呼吸新鲜空气,尽量休养好。可我不喜欢新鲜空气。还有一件事,所有的用人都必须照我的想法去做,因为要是我一生气,我就会生病的。"

虽然他看上去有些怪怪的,可玛丽觉得自己挺喜欢这个孩子。他问了她很多问题,而她就给他讲在印度的生活。

"你几岁了?"他突然问道。

"我 10 岁了,你也是,"玛丽回答,一时说漏了嘴,"因为你出生时花园的门就被锁上,钥匙也被埋起来了,我知道那是 10 年前的事。"

柯林从床上坐起来,一副好奇的样子。"什么门?谁把它锁上的?钥匙在哪儿?我要看看。我要让用人告诉我它在什么地方。他们会带我去那儿,你也可以来。"

"哦,别这样!请别这样!"玛丽大声说。

cousin *n.* *a child of one's aunt or uncle.* 表兄(妹)。**medicine** *n.* *a substance that you take to treat an illness.* 药。

57

Colin stared at her. 'Don't you want to see it?'

'Yes, but if you make them open the door, it will never be a secret again. You see, if only *we* know about it, if we — if we can find the key, we can go and play there every day. We can help the garden come alive again. And no one will know about it — except us!'

'I see,' said Colin slowly. 'Yes, I'd like that. It'll be our secret. I've never had a secret before.'

'And perhaps,' added Mary cleverly, 'we can find a boy to push you in your wheelchair, if you can't walk, and we can go there together without any other people. You'll feel better outside. I know I do.'

'I'd like that,' he said dreamily. 'I think I'd like fresh air, in a secret garden.'

Then Mary told him about the moor, and Dickon, and Ben Weatherstaff, and the robin, and Colin listened to it all with great interest. He began to smile and look much happier.

'I like having you here,' he said. 'You must come and see me every day. But I'm tired now.'

'I'll sing you a song. My servant Kamala used to do that in India,' said Mary, and very soon Colin was asleep.

The next afternoon Mary visited Colin again, and he seemed very pleased to see her. He had sent his nurse away and had told nobody about Mary's visit. Mary had not told anybody either. They read some of his books together, and told each other stories. They were enjoying themselves and laughing loudly

柯林瞪着她。"难道你不想看看它吗?"

"想,可要是你让他们打开门,它就再也不是个秘密了。你想,如果只有我们知道这事,如果我们——如果我们能找到那把钥匙,我们就能每天都去那儿玩儿了。我们还能让花园重新充满生机,而且谁也不会知道——只有我们!"

"我明白了,"柯林慢条斯理地说。"好吧,我愿意这样。它是我们的秘密,我从来没有过自己的秘密。"

"也许,"玛丽机敏地接着说道,"在你走不动的时候,我们也能找个男孩子用轮椅推着你,我们可以一起去那儿,再也没有别人了。你到外面就会感觉好些的。我就是这样,所以我知道。"

"我愿意这样做,"他满怀憧憬地说,"我想我会喜欢一座秘密花园里的新鲜空气的。"

玛丽接着又给他讲荒原,讲狄肯,讲本·威瑟斯塔夫,还有那只知更鸟。柯林非常新奇地听着这一切,他开始有了笑容,样子开心多了。

"我喜欢你在这儿,"他说,"你得每天来看我,可我这会儿有点儿累了。"

"我给你唱个歌吧。在印度时我的用人卡玛拉就常这样。"玛丽说。柯林很快就睡着了。

第二天下午,玛丽又来看柯林。一见到她,柯林显得很高兴。他已经支走了他的护士,也没有告诉其他人玛丽来过。玛丽同样谁也没有告诉。他们一起看柯林的书,互相讲故事。就在他们自得其乐,放声大笑的时

wheelchair *n. a chair with large wheels that someone who cannot walk uses for moving around.* 轮椅。**dreamily** *adv. in a way that shows you are thinking about pleasant things rather than paying attention.* 迷迷糊糊地,朦胧地。

when suddenly the door opened. Dr Craven and Mrs Medlock came in. They almost fell over in surprise.

'What's happening here?' asked Dr Craven.

Colin sat up straight. To Mary he looked just like an Indian prince. 'This is my cousin, Mary Lennox,' he said calmly. 'I like her. She must visit me often.'

'Oh, I'm sorry, sir,' said poor Mrs Medlock to the doctor. 'I don't know how she discovered him. I told the servants to keep it a secret.'

'Don't be stupid, Medlock,' said the Indian prince coldly. 'Nobody told her. She heard me crying and found me herself. Bring our tea up now.'

'I'm afraid you're getting too hot and excited, my boy,' said Dr Craven. 'That's not good for you. Don't forget you're ill.'

'I *want* to forget!' said Colin. 'I'll be angry if Mary doesn't visit me! She makes me feel better.'

Dr Craven did not look happy when he left the room.

'What a change in the boy, sir!' said the housekeeper. 'He's usually so disagreeable with all of us. He really seems to like that strange little girl. And he does look better.' Dr Craven had to agree.

候,门突然开了。克莱文医生和梅洛太太走了进来,他们都很是吃惊。

"怎么回事?"克莱文医生问道。

柯林坐直身子。在玛丽看来,他就像是个印度王子。"这是我的表妹,玛丽·莲诺丝,"他平静地说,"我喜欢她,她必须经常来看我。"

"哦,真抱歉,先生,"可怜的梅洛太太对医生说,"我不知道她是怎么找到他的,我告诉过用人们要保密的。"

"别傻了,梅洛太太,"印度王子冷冷地说,"谁也没告诉她,她听见我哭就自己找来了。现在去给我们沏点茶来。"

"我恐怕你在发热,过于激动,孩子,"克莱文医生说,"这对你可不好,别忘了你有病。"

"我就想忘掉!"柯林说,"要是不让玛丽来看我我就要生气了!她让我觉得好多了。"

克莱文医生离开的时候看起来很不高兴。

"这孩子变多了,先生!"管家说,"他总是跟我们合不来,他好像真的喜欢这个古怪的小姑娘,而且他看着的确好些了。"克莱文医生不得不同意她的话。

prince *n*. *a male member of a royal family who is not the king*. 王子。**stupid** *adj*. *silly*. 傻的,蠢的。

61

6
Colin is afraid

Because it rained all the next week, Mary went to talk to Colin every day instead of visiting the garden. But she woke early one morning to see the sun shining into her room, and she ran out to the secret garden at once. She did not even wait to have her breakfast. It was beautifully sunny and warm, and a thousand more shoots were pushing their way out of the ground. Dickon was already there, digging hard, with the crow and a young fox beside him.

'Have you seen the robin?' he asked Mary. The little bird was flying busily backwards and forwards as fast as he could, carrying pieces of dry grass.

'He's building a nest!' whispered Mary. They watched the robin for a moment. Then Mary said,

'I must tell you something. You probably know about Colin Craven, don't you? Well, I've met him, and I'm going to help him to get better.'

'That's good news.' There was a big smile on Dickon's honest face. 'We all knew he was ill.'

'He's afraid he'll have a crooked back like his father. I think that's what's making him ill.'

'Perhaps we can bring him here and let him rest under the trees. That'll do him good. That's what we'll do.'

6　柯林害怕了

　　由于接下来下了一个星期的雨，玛丽没有去花园，而是每天去和柯林聊天。可一天早晨她很早就醒了，看见阳光洒进她的房间，她立即跑出去来到秘密花园，连早餐也没来得及吃。天气暖和，阳光明媚，无数的嫩牙拱出地面，狄肯已经在那儿了，正起劲地挖着土，他的身边有一只乌鸦和一只小狐狸。

　　"看见知更鸟了吗?"他问玛丽。小鸟正忙碌地飞前飞后衔着枯叶。

　　"它在筑巢呢!"玛丽低声道。他们看了一会儿，然后玛丽说：

　　"我得告诉你一件事。你可能听说过柯林·克莱文，是吗? 我见过他了，而且我要帮助他好起来。"

　　"这可是好消息，"狄肯质朴的脸上露出了开心的笑容，"我们都知道他有病。"

　　"他是害怕会像他父亲那样驼背，我看这就是他生病的原因。"

　　"也许我们可以带他来这儿，让他在树下休息。那会对他有好处，而那正是我们要做的。"

fox　*n. a wild animal similar to a small dog, with red-brown fur, a pointed face, and a thick tail.* 狐狸。**nest**　*n. a structure that birds make to keep their eggs and babies in.*（鸟）巢，窝。**honest** *adj. not telling lies or cheating people, and obeying the law.* 诚实的，老实的。

They had a lot of gardening and planting to do and Mary did not have time to visit Colin that day. When she came back to the house in the evening, Martha told her that the servants had had trouble with Colin.

'He's been very bad-tempered all afternoon with all of us, because you didn't come, miss.'

'Well, I was busy. He'll have to learn not to be so selfish,' replied Mary coldly. She forgot how selfish *she* had been when she was ill in India. 'I'll go and see him now.'

When she went into his room, he was lying in bed, looking tired. He did not turn to look at her.

'What's the matter with you?' she asked crossly.

'My back aches and my head hurts. Why didn't you come this afternoon?'

'I was working in the garden with Dickon.'

'I won't let that boy come to the garden if you stay with him instead of talking to me!'

Mary suddenly became very angry. 'If you send Dickon away, I'll never come into this room again!'

'You'll have to, if I say so. I'll make the servants bring you in here.'

'Oh, will you, prince! But no one can make me talk to you. I won't look at you. I'll stare at the floor!'

'You selfish girl!' cried Colin.

'You're more selfish than I am. You're the most selfish boy I've ever met!'

他们忙着在花园里修整、种花,所以玛丽一整天没时间去看柯林。当她晚上回到房间时,玛莎告诉她用人们在柯林那儿惹了麻烦了。

　　"他整个下午冲我们所有人发脾气,就因为你没去看他,小姐。"

　　"哦,我很忙。他得学着别这么自私。"玛丽冷冷地说。她忘了她自己在印度生病时有多自私了。"我现在就去看他。"

　　她走进房间时,他正躺在床上,显得很疲倦,没有扭头看她。

　　"你怎么啦?"她不太耐烦地问道。

　　"我后背疼,头也疼。下午你为什么没来?"

　　"我在花园里跟狄肯一起干活儿。"

　　"要是你净跟他在一起不来跟我说话,我就不许那个孩子到花园里来!"

　　玛丽当即就生气了。"你要让狄肯走的话,我就再也不到这儿来了!"

　　"你必须得来,因为我说了让你来,我会叫用人把你叫来。"

　　"哦,是吗? 王子! 可是没人能让我跟你说话呀! 我会连看都不看你,就盯着地板!"

　　"你自私!"柯林叫嚷道。

　　"你比我自私多了。你是我见过的最自私的人!"

'I'm not as selfish as your fine Dickon! He keeps you playing outside when he knows I'm ill and alone!'

Mary had never been so furious. 'Dickon is nicer than any other boy in the world! He's like an angel!'

'An angel! Don't make me laugh! He's just a poor country boy, with holes in his shoes!'

'He's a thousand times better than you are!'

Colin had never argued with anyone like himself in his life, and in fact it was good for him. But now he was beginning to feel sorry for himself.

'I'm always ill,' he said, and started to cry. 'I'm sure my back is a bit crooked. And I'm going to die!'

'No, you're not!' said Mary crossly.

Colin opened his eyes very wide. Nobody had said that to him before. He was angry, but a bit pleased at the same time. 'What do you mean? You know I'm going to die! Everybody says I'm going to die!'

'I don't believe it!' said Mary in her most disagreeable voice. 'You just say that to make people feel sorry for you. You're too horrid to die!'

Colin forgot about his painful back and sat up in bed. 'Get out of the room at once!' he shouted, and threw a book at her.

'I'm going,' Mary shouted in reply, 'and I won't come back!' The door banged shut behind her.

When she reached her own room, she had decided never to tell him her great secret. 'He can stay in his room and die if he

"我可不像你可爱的狄肯那么自私,他明知我一个人在生病,却让你一直在外面陪着他玩!"

玛丽从来没生过这么大的气,"狄肯比世界上任何男孩都好!他像个天使!"

"一个天使!别逗了!他不过是个乡下的穷孩子,鞋底还漏着窟窿!"

"他比你好上一千倍!"

柯林长这么大从未同跟自己个性相近的人吵过架,这实际上对他有好处。可这会儿他觉得自己可怜极了。

"我老是生病,"他一边说一边哭起来,"我肯定我的背有点驼了,而且我就快死了!"

"不,你不会的!"玛丽不耐烦了。

柯林睁大了眼睛,以前从来没人这么说过他。他生气了,可同时又有点儿高兴。"你什么意思?你知道我就要死了!每个人都说我快死了!"

"我不信!"玛丽说,声音很刺耳,"你这么说只是想要别人可怜你。你怕死,你不敢去死!"

柯林忘了背疼的事,从床上坐起来,"马上从这儿滚出去!"他吼道,把一本书朝她扔过来。

"我这就走。"玛丽大声说,"我再也不会来了!"她撞上门走了。

回到自己的房间后,她下决心永远不告诉他自己的大秘密。"他可以待在他的房间

angel *n. a spirit that in some religions is believed to live in heaven with God.* 天使。**horrid** *adj. causing horror; dreadful.* 恐怖的,可怕的。**painful** *adj. making you feel upset, ashamed, or unhappy.* 痛苦的。

wants!' she thought. But soon she began to remember how ill
he had been, and how frightened he was, frightened that one
day his back would become as crooked as his father's.
'Perhaps... perhaps I'll go back and see him tomorrow!'

That night she was woken by the most terrible screams that
she had ever heard. Servants were opening and shutting doors
and running about.

'It's Colin!' thought Mary. 'He'll go on screaming until he
makes himself really ill! How selfish he is! Somebody should
stop him!'

Just then Martha ran into the room. 'We don't know what
to do!' she cried. 'He likes you, miss! Come and see if you can
make him calmer, please!'

'Well, I'm very cross with him,' said Mary, and jumped out
of bed. 'I'm going to stop him!'

'That's right,' said Martha. 'He needs someone like you, to
argue with. It'll give him something new to think about.'

Mary ran into Colin's room, right up to his bed.

'Stop screaming!' she shouted furiously. 'Stop at once! I
hate you! Everybody hates you! You'll die if you go on
screaming like this, and I hope you will!'

The screams stopped immediately. This was the first time
that anyone had spoken so angrily to Colin, and he was
shocked. But he went on crying quietly to himself.

'My back's becoming crooked, I can feel it! I know I'm going to die!' Large tears ran down his face.

里,要死就死吧!"她想。可马上她又想起他曾病得那么厉害,他是那么恐惧,担心有一天他的背会像父亲一样驼。"也许……也许明天我会回去看看他!"

这天夜里她被从未听过的恐怖叫声惊醒。用人们开门又关门,跑来跑去。

"是柯林!"玛丽想,"他会不停地叫下去,直到真弄出病来!他多么自私啊!该有人去制止他!"

这时玛莎跑进她的房里,"我们不知道该怎么办!"她叫着,"他喜欢你,小姐!去看看你能不能让他安静下来,好吗?"

"好吧,我烦死他了,"玛丽说着从床上跳下来,"我得去制止他!"

"没错,"玛莎说,"他需要像你这样的人,一起吵吵嘴,这能给他点新鲜的东西让他去琢磨。"

玛丽跑到他的房间,径直走到床前。

"别叫啦!"她气冲冲地喊道,"马上停住!我讨厌你!人人都讨厌你!你再这么喊下去就会死的,我希望你死!"

喊叫声立即停住了。这可是第一次有人这么气愤地对柯林说话,他被吓坏了。不过他还是在小声哭着。

"我的背开始驼了,我能感觉到!我知道我就要死了!"大颗的泪珠从他的脸上流了下来。

scream *v.* *make a loud high cry.* 尖叫。 **immediately** *adv.* *without delay.* 立即,马上。

69

'Don't be stupid!' cried Mary. 'There's nothing the matter with your horrid back! Martha, come here and help me look at his back!'

Martha and Mrs Medlock were standing at the door, staring at Mary, their mouths half open. They both looked very frightened. Martha came forward to help, and Miss Mary looked carefully at Colin's thin white back, up and down. Her face was serious and angry at the same time. The room was very quiet.

'There's nothing wrong with your back!' she said at last. 'Nothing at all! It's as straight as mine!'

Only Colin knew how important those crossly spoken, childish words were. All his life he had been afraid to ask about his back, and his terrible fear had made him ill. Now an angry little girl told him his back was straight, and he believed her. He was no longer afraid.

They were both calmer now. He gave Mary his hand. 'I think — I'm almost sure I will live, if we can go out in the garden together sometimes. I'm very tired now. Will you stay with me until I go to sleep?'

The servants went out very quietly.

'I'll tell you all about the secret garden,' whispered Mary. 'I think it's full of roses and beautiful flowers. Birds like making their nests there because it's so quiet and safe. And perhaps our robin...'

But Colin was already asleep.

The next day Mary met Dickon as usual in the secret

"别傻了!"玛丽叫道,"这跟你可怕的背没关系! 玛莎,过来让我看看他的背!"

玛莎和梅洛太太都站在门边,瞪着玛丽,嘴巴半张着。看来她们都给吓坏了。玛莎走过来帮忙,玛丽小姐上上下下仔细看了柯林那消瘦苍白的脊背,神色严肃,同时又很生气。房间里很静。

"你的脊背一点毛病也没有!"她最后说道,"什么也没有,像我的背一样直!"

只有柯林明白这些带着怒气说出的孩子气的话有多么重要。他长这么大一直都不敢问起自己的脊背,而他的恐惧总是让他病歪歪的。现在这个愤怒的小姑娘告诉他,说他的脊背是直的,而他相信她。他再也不怕了。

他们俩这会儿都安静多了,他把手伸给玛丽。"我想——要是我们哪天能到花园里去的话,我几乎可以肯定我会活下去的。我现在很累了,你能等我睡着后再走吗?"

用人们悄悄地退了出去。

"我要告诉你秘密花园的事,"玛丽低声说,"我想里面满是玫瑰和美丽的花儿,鸟儿喜欢在里面筑巢是因为那儿宁静、安全。而且也许我们的知更鸟……"

可柯林已经睡着了。

第二天玛丽像往常一样在秘密花园里

childish *adj*. *behaving in a silly and annoying way, like a small child*. 小孩子气的。**as usual** 同往常一样。

garden, and told him about Colin. Mary loved Dickon's York-shire dialect and was trying to learn it herself. She spoke a little now.

'We mun get poor Colin out here in th'sunshine—an'we munnot lose no time about it!'

Dickon laughed. 'Well done! I didn't know you could speak Yorkshire! You're right. We must bring Colin to the garden as soon as we can.'

So that afternoon she went to see Colin.

'I'm sorry I said I'd send Dickon away,' he said. 'I hated you when you said he was like an angel!'

'Well, he's a funny kind of angel, but he understands wild animals better than anyone.' Suddenly, Mary knew that this was the right moment to tell him. She caught hold of his hands. 'Colin, this is important. Can you keep a secret?'

'Yes—yes!' he whispered excitedly. 'What is it?'

'We've found the door into the secret garden!'

'Oh Mary! Will I live long enough to see it?'

'Of course you will! Don't be stupid!' said Mary crossly. But it was a very natural thing to say, and they both laughed.

Colin told Mrs Medlock and the doctor that he wanted to go out in his wheelchair. At first the doctor was worried the boy would get too tired, but when he heard that Dickon would push the wheelchair, he agreed.

'Dickon's a sensible boy,' he told Colin. 'But don't forget—'

见到狄肯,告诉了他柯林的事。玛丽喜欢狄肯的约克郡口音,所以努力在学它,她现在已经能说一点了。

"我们得把可怜的柯林弄到这儿来晒晒太阳——我们不能再耽搁了!"

狄肯笑了,"你说得不错呀!我还不知道你会说约克郡的话!没错,我们得尽快带柯林到花园里来。"

于是下午她来看柯林。

"很抱歉我说过让狄肯走的话,"他说,"你说他像个天使,我就讨厌你了。"

"嗯,他是那种有趣的天使,而且他比任何人都了解那些动物。"这时玛丽觉得是告诉他的时候了,她握住他的手,"柯林,这很重要,你能保守秘密吗?"

"能——能!"他兴奋地小声说道,"是什么?"

"我们找到了进秘密花园的门!"

"哦,玛丽!我能活着看看它吗?"

"当然能!别傻了!"玛丽不耐烦了,可这么说又非常自然,于是两人都笑了。

柯林告诉梅洛太太和医生他想坐轮椅出去。开始医生担心他会累着,可当他听说狄肯会用轮椅推着他时,他同意了。

"狄肯是个懂事的孩子,"他对柯林说,"但是别忘了——"

mun = must; in th'sunshine = in the sunshine; an'we munnot = and we must not. 约克郡方言。**understand** *v. know what someone or something means.* 理解,明白。**catch hold of** *seize; grasp.* 抓住,握住。

'I've told you, I *want* to forget that I'm ill,' said Colin in his prince's voice. 'Don't you understand? It's because my cousin makes me forget that I feel better when I'm with her.'

"我告诉过你,我就是想忘了我有病,"柯林用他那王子般的口气说,"你不明白吗?就是因为我表妹让我忘掉我有病,跟她在一起我才觉得好些的。"

7
Colin and the garden

Of course, it was most important that no one should see Colin, Mary, or Dickon entering the secret garden. So Colin gave orders to the gardeners that they must all keep away from that part of the garden in future.

The next afternoon Colin was carried downstairs by a man servant, and put in his wheelchair outside the front door. Dickon arrived, with his crow, two squirrels and the fox, and started pushing the wheelchair gently away from the house, and into the gardens. Mary walked beside the chair.

Spring had really arrived now and it seemed very exciting to Colin, who had lived indoors for so long. He smelt the warm air from the moor, and watched the little white clouds in the blue sky. In a very short time he heard Mary say, 'This is where I found the key... and this is the door... and this... this is the secret garden!'

Colin covered his eyes with his hands until he was inside the four high walls, and the door was shut again. Then he looked round at the roses climbing the old red walls, the pink and white flowers on the fruit trees, and the birds and the butterflies everywhere. The sun warmed his face, and he suddenly knew he felt different.

'Mary! Dickon!' he cried. 'I'm going to get better! I'm

7 柯林在花园里

当然,重要的是不能让人见到柯林、玛丽和狄肯进秘密花园里面去。所以柯林吩咐园丁们以后不准到那片花园去。

第二天下午,柯林由一个男仆抱下楼放在大门外的轮椅上。狄肯来了,带着他的乌鸦、两只松鼠和狐狸,开始慢慢推着轮椅离开房子到花园里去。玛丽在旁边跟着。

春天现在真的来了,而柯林已经在房间里生活了那么久,所以显得十分激动。他闻到荒原上飘来的温暖的气息,看到小朵的白云在蓝天上浮动。很快,他听见玛丽小声说:"我就是在这儿找到钥匙的……门在这儿……这儿……这就是秘密花园!"

柯林用手捂住眼睛,直到进了那四堵高大的围墙里才松开,门又被关上了。然后他四周看了看,看见玫瑰爬满了古老的红砖墙,果树上开着粉色和白色的花儿,到处都是鸟儿和蝴蝶。阳光暖暖地照在他的脸上,他顿时感到自己与以往不一样了。

"玛丽!狄肯!"他喊着,"我会好起来

enter *v. come or go into.* 进入。**smell** *v. notice or recognize the smell of something; experience the smell of something by putting your nose close to it.* 闻,嗅。**butterfly** *n. a flying insect with large colourful wings.* 蝴蝶。

going to live for ever and ever and ever!'

As Dickon pushed the wheelchair all round the garden, he told Colin the names of all the plants. The sun shone, the birds sang, and in every corner of the garden there was something interesting to look at. The three children talked and laughed, and by the end of the afternoon all three were speaking Yorkshire together.

'I'll come back here every afternoon,' said Colin. 'I want to watch things growing.'

'Soon you'll be strong enough to walk and dig. You'll be able to help us with the gardening,' said Dickon kindly.

'Do you really think I'll be able to... to walk and... dig?' asked Colin.

'Of course you will. You've got legs, like us!'

'But they're not very strong,' answered Colin. 'They shake, and... and I'm afraid to stand on them.'

'When you want to use them, you'll be able to,' said Dickon. The garden was quiet for a moment.

Suddenly Colin said, 'Who's that?' Mary turned her head, and noticed Ben Weatherstaff's angry face looking at her over the garden wall.

'What are you doing in that garden, young miss?' he shouted. He had not seen Colin or Dickon.

'The robin showed me the way, Ben,' she replied.

'You... you—' He stopped shouting and his mouth dropped open as he saw Dickon pushing a boy in a wheelchair over the

的！我会永远永远活下去！"

狄肯推着轮椅在花园里转着，告诉柯林所有植物的名字，阳光明媚，鸟儿歌唱，花园的每一个角落都有有趣的东西可看。三个孩子有说有笑，到了傍晚就都说起约克郡话来。

"我每天下午都要来，"柯林说，"我要看着它们生长。"

"你很快就会强壮起来，能自己走路，自己挖土。你还能帮我们收拾园子。"狄肯友好地说道。

"你真的觉得我能……能走路，还能……挖土？"柯林问。

"你当然能！你有腿，跟我们一样！"

"可是我的腿没有劲，"柯林答道，"总是不稳，我……我不敢站起来。"

"你想用它们时，你就能。"狄肯说。花园里有一刻非常安静。

突然，柯林说："那是谁？"玛丽转过头，看见本·威瑟斯塔夫生气的眼睛正从围墙上边望着她。

"你在花园里干嘛，小姐？"他吼道，他没看见柯林和狄肯。

"知更鸟带我来的，本。"她回答。

"你……你——"当他看见狄肯在对面的草地上用轮椅推着个男孩时，他不再吼叫，嘴巴也张得老大。

grass towards him.

'Do you know who I am?' asked the boy in the chair.

Old Ben stared. 'You've got your mother's eyes,' he said in a shaking voice. 'Yes, I know you. You're Mr Craven's son, the little boy with the crooked back.'

Colin forgot that he had ever had backache. 'My back's as straight as yours is!' he shouted.

Ben stared and stared. He only knew what he had heard from the servants. 'You haven't got a crooked back?' he asked. 'Or crooked legs?'

That was too much. Colin was furious, and it made him feel strong.

'Come here, Dickon!' he shouted, and threw off his blanket. Dickon was by his side in a second. Mary felt sick with fear. Could Colin stand?

Then Colin's thin feet were on the grass and he was standing, holding Dickon's arm. He looked strangely tall, and he held his head very high.

'Look at me!' he shouted at Ben. 'Just look at me!'

'He's as straight as any boy in Yorkshire!' said Dickon.

Tears were running down Ben's brown old face. 'They said you were going to die!' he whispered.

'Well, you can see that's not true,' said Colin. 'Now, get down from the wall and come here. I want to talk to you. You've got to help us keep the garden a secret.'

'Yes, sir,' said old Ben, as he dried his eyes.

"知道我是谁吗?"轮椅上的男孩问。

本瞪大了眼睛,"你的眼睛跟你妈妈的一模一样,"他说,声音有点发抖,"是啊,我认识你,你是克莱文先生的儿子,那个驼背的小男孩。"

柯林忘了自己曾一度背疼。他嚷道:"我的背跟你的一样直!"

本从上到下仔细打量。他只是听仆人们说起过。"你的背不驼?"他问道,"你不是罗圈腿?"

这可太过分了。柯林生气了,这反而让他觉得强壮起来。

"过来,狄肯!"他叫道,甩掉了盖毯,狄肯立刻来到他身旁,玛丽感到有点担心,柯林能站起来吗?

柯林瘦弱的脚放在草地上,扶着狄肯的胳膊站了起来。他看上去异常高大,头高高地扬着。

"看我!"他冲本喊道,"看看我呀!"

"他像约克郡的任何一个男孩一样直!"狄肯说。

泪水从本那棕色而苍老的脸上滑落下来。"他们说你要死了!"他小声说。

"那么,你该知道那不是真的,"柯林说道,"现在从墙上下来到这儿来吧。我想跟你谈谈。你得帮我们保守花园的秘密。"

"好的,先生。"本说着,一边擦干了泪水。

blanket *n. a thick cover made of wool or another material that you use to keep warm in bed.* 毯子。

81

That was the first of many beautiful afternoons in the secret garden. Colin was brought there by Dickon and Mary nearly every day, and he saw all the changes that happened there during the spring and early summer. Ben Weatherstaff, now in the secret, joined them as often as he could.

One day Colin spoke to all of them. 'Listen, everybody. I think there's something like magic that makes gardens grow and things happen. Perhaps if I believe in it, the magic will make me strong. Let's all sit down in a circle and ask the magic to work.'

So they all sat on the grass in a circle, Dickon with his crow, his fox and the two squirrels, Mary, Colin, and Ben. Colin repeated these words several times. 'The sun's shining. That's the magic. Being strong. That's the magic. Magic! Help me! Magic! Help me!'

At last Colin stopped. 'Now I'm going to walk round the garden,' he said, and took Dickon's arm. Slowly he walked from one wall to another, followed closely by Mary and Ben. And when he had walked all the way round, he said, 'You see! I can walk now! The magic worked!'

'It's wonderful!' cried Mary. 'Your father will think he is dreaming when he sees you!'

'I won't tell him yet. I'm going to keep it a secret from everybody. I'll come to the garden and walk and run a little more every day until I'm as healthy as any other boy. Then, when my father comes home, I'll walk up to him and say, "Here I

这是秘密花园中第一个美丽的下午,这样的下午以后还有很多。柯林几乎每天都由狄肯和玛丽带到这儿,他看到了春天和初夏这里的所有变化。本·威瑟斯塔夫,现在也保守着这个秘密,一有空就加入他们。

一天,柯林对大家说:"你们大家听我说。我想是什么魔法使花园里的植物生长,使很多事情发生。或许要是我相信,魔法也会使我变得强壮起来。咱们坐下来围成圈请魔法显灵吧!"

于是他们围坐在草地上,狄肯和他的乌鸦、狐狸以及两只松鼠,玛丽、柯林和本。柯林一连几遍地重复说着:"阳光在照耀,这就是魔法。强壮起来,这就是魔法。魔法!帮帮我!魔法!帮帮我!"

最后柯林停下来。"现在我得在花园里走走了。"他说。于是他扶着狄肯的胳膊,慢慢地从一面墙走到另一面墙,玛丽和本紧紧跟着他们。当他走完一圈时,他说:"看哪!我能走了!魔法显灵了!"

"太棒了!"玛丽叫着,"你父亲看见你一定会以为是在做梦呢!"

"我还不想告诉他。我要保守秘密,不让任何人知道。我要每天都到花园里散步,再跑上一小会儿,直到我像其他人一样健康。到那会儿,等我父亲回家时,我要走到

magic *n. the mysterious power that some people believe can make impossible things happen if you do special actions or say special words.* 魔法,魔力。

am, Father. You see? I'm not going to die!"'

Now began a difficult time for Colin and Mary. Dickon told his mother about it one evening as he was digging the cottage garden.

'You see, mother, they don't want the doctor or the servants to guess that Colin can walk and is getting better. So they have to pretend he's still ill and just as disagreeable as he used to be!'

'If they're running about all day in the fresh air, that'll make them hungry, I should think!'

'Yes, that's the problem. They're both getting fatter and healthier, and they really enjoy their food now. But they have to send some of it back to the kitchen, uneaten. If they eat it all, people will realize how healthy they are! Sometimes they're very hungry!'

'I know what we can do,' said Mrs Sowerby. 'You can take some fresh milk and some of my newly baked bread to the garden in the mornings. If they have that, it'll do them a lot of good ! What a game those children are playing!' And she laughed until tears came to her eyes.

One afternoon when they were all working in the garden, the door opened and a woman came quietly in.

'It's Mother!' cried Dickon, and ran towards her. 'I told her where the door was, because I knew she would keep the secret.'

Colin held out his hand to her. 'I've wanted to see you for a

他面前,说:'我在这儿,爸爸。你看到了吗?
我不会死的!'"

这可给玛丽和柯林出了难题。狄肯一
天晚上在挖屋前的菜园时把这事告诉了妈
妈。

"您看,妈妈,他们不想让医生或用人猜
出柯林能走路,而且身体也好多了。所以他
们假装他还病着,而且还像从前一样不讨人
喜欢!"

"要是他们整天跑来跑去,呼吸新鲜空
气,那样他们会感到饿的,我想。"

"是啊,就是这件事。他们俩都长胖了,
也健康了,而且很能吃饭。可是他们却不
得不剩下一些送回厨房,要是都吃光了,人
家就会知道他们很健康! 所以,他们有时饿
得很厉害!"

"我知道我们能做些什么,"索尔比太太
说,"上午你带点新鲜的牛奶和我刚烤好的
面包到花园去,吃了这些会对他们有很大好
处的! 孩子们这是在玩什么把戏啊!"她笑
得眼泪都流出来了。

一天下午,他们正在花园里干活儿,门
开了,一个女人悄悄走了进来。

"是妈妈!"狄肯喊道,跑了过去,"我告
诉了她门在哪儿,因为我知道她会保密的。"

柯林向她伸出手,说:"我一直都想见到
您。"

run about　　四处跑。

85

long time,' he said.

'Dear boy!' Susan Sowerby whispered, holding his hand. 'You're so like your mother!'

'Do you think,' asked Colin carefully, 'that will make my father like me?'

'I'm sure it will,' she answered warmly. 'He must see you—he must come home now.'

'You see how healthy the boy is, Susan?' asked old Ben. 'Look how strong and straight his legs are now!'

'Yes,' she laughed. 'Playing and working outside, and eating good Yorkshire food, has made him strong. And Miss Mary too,' she added, turning to Mary. 'Mrs Medlock heard that your mother was a pretty woman. You'll soon be as pretty as she was.'

'Do you believe in magic?' Colin asked her.

'I do,' she answered, 'but everybody gives it a different name. It makes the sun shine and the seeds grow — and it has made you healthy.'

She sat down on the grass and stayed for a while, talking and laughing with the children in the quiet, sunny garden. When she stood up to leave, Colin suddenly put out a hand to her.

'I wish — you were my mother!' he whispered.

Mrs Sowerby put her arms round him and held him to her. 'Dear boy! You're as close to your mother as you could be, here in her garden. And your father'll come back soon!'

"好孩子!"苏珊·索尔比小声说着,握住他的手,"你长得可真像你妈妈。"

"您觉得,"柯林小心地问道,"这会让我父亲喜欢我吗?"

"我肯定他会的。"她热情地答道,"他得看看你——他现在应该回家了。"

"苏珊,瞧这孩子多健康啊!"本说,"看他的腿,现在又直又结实!"

"是啊,"她笑了,"在外面玩,在外面干活,加上约克郡的美食,这就让他壮实起来了。玛丽小姐也是这样。"她加了一句,转向玛丽。"梅洛太太听说你妈妈很漂亮,你很快也会像她一样漂亮的。"

"您相信魔法吗?"柯林问她。

"相信。"她回答,"不过每个人都给它起了个不同的名字。它使阳光照耀,种子生长——同样也让你健康。"

她在草地上坐了一会儿,和孩子们在洒满阳光、宁静的花园里说笑着。她站起身临走的时候,柯林向她伸出了手。

"我真希望——您是我的妈妈!"他小声说。

索尔比太太把他搂在怀里:"好孩子!在你妈妈的花园里,你离她要多近有多近。而且,你爸爸也快回来了!"

8

Mr Craven comes home

While the secret garden was returning to life, a man with high, crooked shoulders was wandering round the most beautiful places in Europe. For ten years he had lived this lonely life, his heart full of sadness and his head full of dark dreams. Everywhere he went, he carried his unhappiness with him like a black cloud. Other travellers thought he was half mad or a man who could not forget some terrible crime. His name was Archibald Craven.

But one day, as he sat by a mountain stream, he actually looked at a flower, and for the first time in ten years he realized how beautiful something living could be. The valley seemed very quiet as he sat there, staring at the flower. He felt strangely calm.

'What is happening to me?' he whispered. 'I feel different—I almost feel I'm alive again!'

At that moment, hundreds of miles away in Yorkshire, Colin was seeing the secret garden for the first time, and saying, 'I'm going to live for ever and ever and ever!' But Mr Craven did not know this.

That night, in his hotel room, he slept better than usual. As the weeks passed, he even began to think a little about his home and his son. One evening in late summer, as he was

8 克莱文先生回家了

当秘密花园恢复着生机的时候,一个高大、驼背的男人正在欧洲最美的地方游荡。10年来他就是过着这种孤独的生活,他的心中充满了悲凉,脑海也被黑暗的恶梦所占据。他每到一处,情绪总是忧郁的,像被一团黑色的云笼罩着。别的游客觉得他是半个疯子,或是个无法忘掉某种恐怖罪行的人。他的名字就是阿奇伯德·克莱文。

但是有一天,当他坐在山谷中的一条小溪旁时,他注视着一朵花,10年来他第一次意识到生命可以是这么美丽。山谷非常幽静,他坐在那儿,凝视着那朵花,心中异常的平静。

"我怎么了?"他低声说,"我感觉不一样了——我几乎觉得自己又活了!"

也就在那一刻,在几百英里外的约克郡,柯林第一次见到了秘密花园,正在说着:"我会永远永远活下去!"但克莱文先生并不知道这些。

那天夜里,在旅店的房间里,他睡得比平时香。几周过去了,他甚至开始有点想家,有点想他的儿子。一个夏末的晚上,他

sadness *n. a feeling of being unhappy, especially because something bad has happened.* 忧伤,悲伤。

sitting quietly beside a lake, he felt the strange calmness again. He fell asleep, and had a dream that seemed very real. He heard a voice calling him. It was sweet and clear and happy, the voice of his young wife.

'Archie! Archie! Archie!'

'My dear!' He jumped up. 'Where are you?'

'In the garden!' called the beautiful voice.

And then the dream ended. In the morning, when he woke, he remembered the dream.

'She says she's in the garden!' he thought. 'But the door's locked and the key's buried.'

That morning he received a letter from Susan Sowerby. In it she asked him to come home, but she did not give a reason. Mr Craven thought of his dream, and decided to return to England immediately. On the long journey back to Yorkshire, he was thinking about Colin.

'I wonder how he is! I wanted to forget him, because he makes me think of his mother. He lived, and she died! But perhaps I've been wrong. Susan Sowerby says I should go home, so perhaps she thinks I can help him.'

When he arrived home, he found the housekeeper very confused about Colin's health.

'He's very strange, sir,' said Mrs Medlock. 'He looks better, it's true, but some days he eats nothing at all, and other days he eats just like a healthy boy. He used to scream even at the idea of fresh air, but now he spends all his time outside in

静静地坐在湖边,再次感到那种奇异的平静。他睡着了,做了一个非常真切的梦。他听见一个声音在叫他,声音甜美、清晰而欢快,那是他年轻的妻子的声音。

"阿奇!阿奇!阿奇!"

"亲爱的!"他跳起来,"你在哪儿?"

"在花园里!"那美丽的声音说。

然后梦就醒了。他早晨醒来时,还记得那个梦。

"她说她在花园里!"他思索着,"可是门是锁着的,钥匙也埋起来了。"

那天上午他收到了苏珊·索尔比的来信。信上她请他回去,却没说明为什么。克莱文先生想起他的梦,决定立刻动身回英国。在回约克郡的漫长路途中,他想起了柯林。

"不知道他怎么样了!我想忘记他,因为他总是让我想起他的妈妈。他活着,可她却死了!也许是我错了。苏珊·索尔比说我应该回家,也许她是想让我帮助柯林。"

他回到家里,发现管家对柯林的身体状况大为不解。

"他很怪,先生,"梅洛太太说,"他看上去好些了,真的,可有时他什么都不吃,有时又吃得像健康的孩子一样。以前只要提到新鲜空气他就要尖叫,可现在他每天都坐

receive *v. to get something that someone gives or sends to you*. 收到。

91

his wheelchair, with Miss Mary and Dickon Sowerby. He's in the garden at the moment.'

'In the garden!' repeated Mr Craven. Those were the words of the dream! He hurried out of the house and towards the place which he had not visited for so long. He found the door with the climbing plant over it, and stood outside, listening, for a moment.

'Surely I can hear voices inside the garden?' he thought. 'Aren't there children whispering, laughing, running in there? Or am I going mad?'

And then the moment came, when the children could not stay quiet. There was wild laughing and shouting, and the door was thrown open. A boy ran out, a tall, healthy, handsome boy, straight into the man's arms. Mr Craven stared into the boy's laughing eyes.

'Who—What? Who?' he cried.

Colin had not planned to meet his father like this. But perhaps this was the best way, to come running out with his cousin and his friend.

'Father,' he said, 'I'm Colin. You can't believe it! I can't believe it myself. It was the garden, and Mary and Dickon and the magic, that made me well. We've kept it a secret up to now. Aren't you happy, Father? I'm going to live for ever and ever and ever!'

Mr Craven put his hands on the boy's shoulders. For a moment he could not speak. 'Take me into the garden, my boy,'

着轮椅去外面,跟玛丽小姐和狄肯·索尔比一起。这会儿他在花园里呢。"

"在花园里!"克莱文先生重复着。那正是梦中听到的话!他冲出房子,奔向他很久都没再去过的地方。他找到被藤蔓遮蔽的门,站在外面,听了一会儿。

"我真的听到里面有声音吗?"他想,"难道那不是孩子们在里面低语、嬉笑、奔跑吗?还是我快要发疯了?"

当孩子们难以保持安静时,这一刻终于到来了。开心的笑声和欢叫声中,门被撞开了,一个高高的、健康漂亮的男孩跑了出来,正好撞进他的怀里。克莱文先生直愣愣地看着孩子欢笑的眼睛。

"谁呀——什么?这是谁呀?"他叫起来。

柯林没想到会这样见到他的父亲。但是同他的表妹和朋友一起跑出来,也许这才是最好的方式。

"爸爸。"他说,"我是柯林。您不会相信的!连我自己都不能相信。是花园、玛丽、狄肯和魔法使我康复的。我们一直保守着这个秘密。爸爸,您不高兴吗?我要永远永远地活下去!"

克莱文先生把手放在孩子肩上,好一会儿说不出话来。最后他说:"带我到花园里去,我的孩子,告诉我这一切是怎么回事。"

up to now　至今,到目前。

93

he said at last, 'and tell me all about it. '

And in the secret garden, where the roses were at their best, and the butterflies were flying from flower to flower in the summer sunshine, they told Colin's father their story. Sometimes he laughed and sometimes he cried, but most of the time he just looked, unbelieving, into the handsome face of the son that he had almost forgotten.

'Now, ' said Colin at the end, 'it isn't a secret any more. I'll never use the wheelchair again. I'm going to walk back with you, Father—to the house. '

And so, that afternoon, Mrs Medlock, Martha, and the other servants had the greatest shock of their lives. Through the gardens towards the house came Mr Craven, looking happier than they had ever seen him. And by his side, with his shoulders straight, his head held high and a smile on his lips, walked young Colin!

在秘密花园中,玫瑰花盛开着,蝴蝶在夏日的阳光下、在花丛中飞舞,他们向柯林的父亲讲述着他们的故事。他时而开怀大笑,时而落泪,更多的时间只是注视着他儿子那英俊的脸庞,不相信这就是他几乎遗忘的那个孩子。

"现在,"柯林最后说道,"这不再是秘密了。我再也用不着轮椅了。爸爸,我要和你一起走——走回家去。"

于是那天下午,梅洛太太、玛莎,还有其他的用人都感受到有生以来从未有过的惊奇,克莱文先生从花园走向房子,脸上露出他们从未见到过的幸福神态。而走在他身边,昂首挺胸、面带微笑的正是年轻的柯林!

unbelieving　*adj*. *not believing*; *doubting*. 不相信的,怀疑的。

Exercises

A Checking your understanding

Chapter 1 *Who said these words in the story?*

1 'We must leave soon!'

2 'Why was I forgotten?'

3 'He's got a crooked back, and he's horrid!'

4 'You must stay out of his way!'

Chapter 2 *Who in this chapter . . .*

1 . . . was cleaning the fireplace in Mary's bedroom?

2 . . . knew a lot about wild animals?

3 . . . buried the key to the secret garden?

4 . . . was a Yorkshire moor man?

Chapters 3 − 4 *Are these sentences true (T) or false (F)?*

1 The door to the secret garden was locked nine years ago.

2 Martha went to visit her family for a week.

3 Mrs Sowerby bought a skipping-rope for Mary.

4 Ben's favourite flowers were roses.

Chapters 5 − 6 *Find answers to these questions in the text.*

1 How did Mary find Colin's room?

2 Why was the robin so busy in the garden?

3 Why did Mary look at Colin's back?

Chapters 7 − 8 *Write answers to these questions.*

1 Why did Colin get better?

2 Who spoke to Mr Craven in his dream?

3 Why did Mr Craven decide to come home?

B Working with language

1 *Put together these beginnings and endings of sentences. Check your answers in Chapter 3.*

1 Mary felt lonelier than ever...

2 I like Dickon,...

3 Are things growing in the garden...

4 Before she came to Yorkshire...

5 As Mary looked at the hole,...

6 She hoped...

7 ...she noticed something almost buried there.

8 ...where he lives?

9 ...when Martha had gone.

10 ...although I've never seen him.

11 ...they weren't all dead.

12 ...she had not liked anybody.

2 *Complete these sentences with information from the story.*

1 Mr Craven buried the key to the secret garden because...

2 Mrs Medlock was angry with Mary when...

3 When Mary asked her uncle for a bit of garden, he...

4 Colin's legs were not very strong, but...

5 While Colin was becoming healthier, his father...

6 Colin told his father the story, and then...

C Activities

1 You are Colin. Write his diary for the day when he first visited the secret garden.
2 Which person do you like, or dislike, most in the story? Why? Write a few sentences to describe this person.
3 What do you think will happen to Mary, Colin, and Dickon in ten years' time? Write another paragraph to finish the story. You could begin like this:

When Colin and Mary were twenty, they still lived at Misselthwaite Manor . . .